The Tropical Asiatic Slipper Orchids

The Tropical Asiatic Slipper Orchids

GENUS PAPHIOPEDILUM

KEITH S. BENNETT

ANGUS
& ROBERTSON
PUBLISHERS

ANGUS & ROBERTSON PUBLISHERS

Unit 4, Eden Park, 31 Waterloo Road,
North Ryde, NSW, Australia 2113, and
16 Golden Square, London W1R 4BN,
United Kingdom

First published in Australia
by Angus & Robertson Publishers in 1984
First published in the United Kingdom
by Angus & Robertson (UK) Ltd in 1985
Reprinted 1986

National Library of Australia
Cataloguing-in-publication data.

Bennett, Keith S. (Keith Stanley), 1922-
   The tropical Asiatic slipper orchids.

   Includes index.

   ISBN 0 207 14887 2.

   1. Paphiopedilum. I. Title.

584'.15

Typeset in English Times by Graphicraft
Typesetters
Printed in Singapore

FOREWORD

For the first time in almost a century, Keith Bennett's *Tropical Asiatic Slipper Orchids* has put within reach of the average hobbyist an inexpensive yet comprehensive guide to the puzzling array of ladyslipper orchid species from the far-flung portions of tropical Asia, which are only now becoming more fully understood.

Since these were regions fraught with great danger and disease a hundred years ago, particularly in the southern Philippines, many species are now being described for the first time. Older works cannot possibly fill in the deficiencies in our knowledge of orchid species as comprehensively as does this modern treatise, which has taken in the botanical discoveries of the past 100 years. Furthermore, works published in recent years and selling for five times the cost of Mr Bennett's work still lack the most up-to-date enumeration of species, as every year one or two completely new species, not previously known to science, make their appearance.

Mr Bennett's guide should serve as a lasting and beautifully illustrated work available to the average greenhouse grower for immediate and handy reference for years to come.

J. A. Fowlie, M. D., Editor
The *Orchid Digest*

CONTENTS

ACKNOWLEDGMENTS

I wish to express my gratitude to the following people who have contributed to the compiling of this book:

Mr John L. Marks, former Registrar General of the Australian Orchid Council, for his preliminary editing and loan of many colour slides.

Mr M. W. Wood, for his advice and permission to quote from his articles in the *Orchid Review*.

The many orchid-growing friends who have shared their knowledge and made plants available for study and photographing.

Professor Wu Zhengyi, Director of the Kunming Institute of Botany, the Academy of Sciences of China, for his kindness in supplying me with descriptions of *P. dianthum* and *P. barbigerum*. Also for sending me the photograph of *P. dianthum* which is reproduced in this book. It is, to my knowledge, the first time this beautiful species has been seen by the western world.

My thanks also to Mrs Li Hen of the above Institute for sending me the descriptions and photographs of *P. armeniacum* and *P. micranthum*.

Lastly, but by no means least, a special acknowledgment to J. A. Fowlie MD, Editor of the *Orchid Digest*. I am deeply grateful to Dr Fowlie for his invaluable botanical help in compiling these notes, for keeping me advised of his latest discoveries in the field and for supplying illustrations for *Paphiopedilum* species *adductum, amabile, bodegomii, boxalli, celebesensis, ciliolare, gardineri, gratrixianum, johorensis, kolopakingii, nigritum, robinsonii, roebbelenii, rothschildianum, sanderianum, stonei, thailandense, victoria-mariae, virens, volonteanum, wardii, wentworthianum, wilhelminiae* and *zieckianum*.

References were made to *Encyclopedia of Cultivated Orchids* by A. D.

Hawkes, *The Orchids* by C. L. Withner, *A Cultural Table of Orchidaceous Plants* by J. Murray Cox, *Sander's List of Orchid Hybrids, A Checklist for the Genus* Paphiopedilum *for 1980–81* by J. H. Asher, Jun., the American *Orchid Digest*, the English *Orchid Review* Ltd (1893–1982), and the *Australian Orchid Review.*

INTRODUCTION

After growing miscellaneous species orchids for over a quarter of a century, it is natural for one to develop a special liking and interest in one particular genus. In my case, it was the genus *Paphiopedilum* which slowly but surely began increasing in numbers and depriving other genera of their rightful bench space. They spread like a benign growth and have now completely dominated every glasshouse. Like a large company after a successful 'take-over' bid, they appear to be smugly contented. I sometimes feel that if a plant of another genus was placed near them, they would be most resentful.

The old cliche, 'beauty lies in the eye of the beholder', is a very true one. No one can deny that modern *Paphiopedilum* hybrids are beautiful in a certain manner. They are huge, well-shaped, and beautifully coloured, but of a vastly different type of beauty to that of the species. To me, the beauty of species lies in their great diversity of shape, colour, and size, in the striking patterns of their foliage, and in their widely spread flowering periods which enable one to admire their beauty throughout the year.

The problem of acquiring some of the rarer species is a challenging one, but, of recent years, some of the commercial nurseries specialising in the genus have built up comprehensive stocks. Many countries have recently banned all exports of their indigenous orchids, making it necessary for future stocks of some members of the genus to be obtained only by growing from seed.

The lack of any publication which describes and illustrates all known members of the genus led me to begin photographing and describing this species some years ago. The plant descriptions have purposefully been written with as little botanical terminology as possible, in order to save the reader from having to constantly refer to a glossary of terms. It is hoped that in some small way this book will assist the novice *Paphiopedilum* grower in the identification and culture of this fascinating genus.

Botanists and orchidists are currently studying the genus in greater depth than has ever been done before and collectors are active in areas which were previously inaccessible. As a result, many new species have recently been described and several 'lost' species have been re-discovered. Some species have been changed to synonyms and some varieties given specific status. Others have been reduced to either subspecies or varieties. Such being the current state of taxonomy, I make no apologies for the fact that some names may be changed during the time that these notes are written.

The two leading publications which print many articles on the genus are the English *Orchid Review*, and the American *Orchid Digest*. Unfortunately, the approach to taxonomy used by these two publications is vastly different and this difference is a source of great contention among *Paphiopedilum* species growers. Basically, the *Orchid Review* tends to group many closely related kinds under one species whereas the *Orchid Digest* splits the group into separate species although the botanical difference between them may be almost indistinguishable. The *Orchid Digest* is currently using chromosome counts to further distinguish between closely related species. (Their *Checklist for the Genus* Paphiopedilum *for 1980–81* includes these chromosome counts.)

A typical example of the different taxonomic approach is a new combination published by Mr M. W. Wood in the *Orchid Review* of May 1976, in which *P. victoria-mariae* is changed to *P. victoria-regina*. In the same paper, *P. chamberlainianum, P. glaucophyllum, P. liemianum,* and *P. primulinum* are reduced to subspecies of *P. victoria-regina*.

These changes, however, are not universally accepted and the American *Orchid Digest* is still using the original names of the taxa. Mr M. W. Wood has kindly allowed me to quote from his articles in the *Orchid Review*, and the above-mentioned paper will be quoted in greater detail elsewhere in these notes.

As such, I choose not to 'take sides' in any taxonomical controversies, but, instead, in the case of contentious species, to list both taxa and so allow the reader to make his own decision as to which school of thought is correct. It can only be hoped that our leading orchidists will soon 'join forces', and, by following established botanical guidelines, arrive at a mutually acceptable taxon for each species.

Although the taxonomy of many species is subject to contention, only one causes controversy as to its correct spelling. This species is *P. fairieanum*, and the controversy concerns the number of 'r's' which the specific epithet should contain.

Although named in honour of the person who first flowered it, a Mr Fairie of Liverpool, there is a possibility that this person spelled his name as Fairrie. However, the original description and many subsequent usages (including Reichenbach in *Xenia orchidacea*, Vol. 11, page 109, 1862) use a single 'r'.

Therefore, basing the decision on long continued usage and original publication with a single 'r' I continue to use the original spelling in these notes.

As previously mentioned, some *Paphiopedilum* species are very closely related and have very slight botanical differences. Typical examples are *P. appletonianum* and *P. wolterianum*, and *P. javanicum*, *P. virens* and *P. purpurascens*. All these species, however, have 'stable' staminodes, that is, their staminodes do not vary within the species, even in plants found growing in different areas. Thus, although they may have other slight botanical differences, their staminodes are the main factor in their identification.

In the case of 'intermediate' species, however, the staminodes are 'unstable' and may vary greatly within the species, depending upon the areas in which they are found. They thus cannot be used as the main factor in their identification. A typical group of 'intermediate' species such as *P. barbatum*, *P. callosum* and *P. sublaeve* may have staminodes which vary widely in plants from different areas.

In the following pages of descriptions and illustrations, the species are listed alphabetically, and not grouped according to their subgenera and sections. I hope this will enable the readers to locate more quickly the species they seek to identify.

Beside the specific epithet is shown the name of the botanist or orchidist who published it under its present name, then the date of publishing. If a species has been transferred from one genus to another, the original author is shown in parentheses, followed by the name of the author who transferred same. This name is not shown in parentheses. Beneath these are given the subgenus and section to which it belongs, then the chromosome count (where available), and finally the synonyms and the area where it has been found.

In the case of species where the taxonomy is contentious, taxa used by both the *Orchid Review* and the *Orchid Digest* are shown and designated by the abbreviations *O.R.* and *O.D.* respectively.

All imperial equivalents of metric measurements given in brackets are approximate.

BOTANICAL CLASSIFICATION

The genus *Paphiopedilum* Pfitz., together with *Selinipedilum* Rchb.f., *Cypripedium* Lindl., and *Phragmipedium* Rolfe, form the subtribe Cypripediliae.

This subtribe is placed in a separate subfamily called the Diandrae, as opposed to all other orchids which are members of the subfamily Monandrae. The reason for this separation is that the four genera which make up the subfamily Diandrae differ widely in floral structure from all other orchid genera. In fact, some orchid authorities have suggested that the group be relegated to a separate family ranking next to the Orchidaceae.

All four genera of the subfamily Diandrae possess two fertile anthers as compared to the single anther found in all other orchids. The staminode, located at the apex of the column, acts as protection for the anthers and stigma. It is often lobed and furnished with hairs and warts and is an important factor in the identification of closely related species. Also the two lateral sepals, which are found in other orchid genera, are fused into one segment known as the ventral sepal or synsepalum in the subfamily Diandrae.

The genus *Paphiopedilum* comprises about 80 species of terrestrial, lithophytic, and epiphytic orchids which are widespread over a vast region extending from India and China, through South-East Asia and Indonesia to New Guinea.

The following classification of various subgenera and sections of the genus *Paphiopedilum* is basically as published in a monograph by the German botanist Ernst Pfitzer in 1903. Many new species have been discovered and described since that date and in these notes the majority of these have been added to the sections which best describe their botanical features.

However, the American *Orchid Digest* has recently published their *Checklist for the Genus* Paphiopedilum *for 1980–81* in which James H. Asher, Jun., and Dr J. A. Fowlie have regrouped species taken from other categories and given them three sections of their own. The following quotes from the *Checklist* explain their reasons for this action:

1. 'The Section *Venustum*: When Pfitzer first published his work, *P. wardii* and *P. sukhakulii* were plants undescribed to science. Hence, it was reasonable to try to "lump" *P. venustum* into a group where it would fit, and the group selected by Pfitzer was *Spathopetalum* Section. With the advent of cytogenetic studies, and the discovery of two additional species with marbled foliage and descent from a once common ancestor, it is elected here to best treat these as a new section, *Venustum*.'

2. 'It also requires no great difficulty in further segregating *P. hookerae* and *P. volonteanum* as something completely apart on their own and the former has three proven geographic races and the latter two, and not all the colonies have yet been studied extensively where they occur. Therefore, Section *Hookerae*, after the first named, would appear reasonable for this latter group.'

3. 'The Section *Mastersianum* certainly nicely takes in the *P. went-worthianum* from Bougainville as it does *P. zieckianum* from the Vogelkopf Peninsula of north-west New Guinea and *P. mastersianum* from Ambon Is.'

There are three distinct subgenera of *Paphiopedilum*:

1. *Brachypetalum* Hallier

All the species comprising this subgenus are distinguished by having lips which lack auricles. They have in-rolled lip margins, are of dwarf habit and have thick, mottled leaves, with purplish undersides. They are all found in limestone areas, and thus respond well to the addition of a little dolomite in their growing medium.

2. *Anotopedilum* Pfitz.

The distinguishing features of members of this subgenus are lips without auricles, petals extremely elongated and narrow, bright green untessellated leaves, and long flower scapes bearing multiple flowers which all open together.

3. *Otopedilum* Pfitz.
All members of this subgenus have lips with conspicuous auricles and elongated petals. Their elongation, however, is not as pronounced as in subgenus *Anotopedilum*.

NOTE: I am grateful for Mr M. W. Wood's explanation that this subgenus should be correctly called subgenus *Paphiopedilum* because the subgenus which contains the type species should be named after the genus. The type species is *P. insigne* which is included in this subgenus. However, as this subgenus is still very widely known as *Otopedilum*, I feel that the hobbyist grower would be even more confused if the name was changed in these notes. Hopefully, a more scientific work will soon deal with this matter in greater detail.

In the following classification, the two latter subgenera are further divided into sections, each of which is numbered in Roman numerals and given a Greek or Latin name which describes a botanical feature common to each section:

1. *Brachypetalum*
This subgenus has no separate sections and comprises:
P. x. *ang-thong* Fowl., *nat. hybd.* 1980 (O.D.)
P. armeniacum
P. bellatulum
P. concolor
P. delenatii
P. godefroyae
P. leucochilum (O.D.) (*P. godefroyae* var. *leucochilum*)
P. niveum

2. Subgenus *Anotopedilum*. Section II *Gonatopetalum*
Is so named because of a curious knee-like bend in the staminode and comprises only one species:
P. rothschildianum

Subgenus *Anotopedilum*. Section III *Coryopedilum*
This name refers to the distinctive helmet-shaped lip. Members of this subgenus are:
P. adductum
P. bodegomii
P. gardineri
P. glanduliferum
P. laevigatum
P. philippinense
P. praestans
P. randsii
P. roebbelenii
P. sanderianum
P. wilhelminiae

Subgenus *Anotopedilum*. Section IV *Prenipedilum*
This section is distinctive in having a lip which droops forward and projects from the other segments. It consists of only one species:
P. stonei

3. Subgenus *Otopedilum*. Section V *Mystropetalum*
This name refers to the distinctive ladle shape of the petals in this section:
P. parishii
P. dianthum

Subgenus *Otopedilum*. Section VI *Pardalopetalum*
From the Greek word, *pardalis*, meaning 'leopard', this name describes the distinctive spotted petals of the members of this section. They are further distinguished by having thick leaves and multi-flowered scapes:
P. lowii
P. haynaldianum

Subgenus *Otopedilum*. Section VII *Cochlopetalum*
From the Greek word, *kochlas*, meaning 'spiral shell', this name describes the spiral or twisted petals which distinguish the members of this group:
P. victoria-mariae

P. chamberlainianum
P. glaucophyllum
P. moquetteanum
P. chamberlainianum subsp. *liemiana*
P. chamberlainianum forma *primulinum* var. *flavum*
P. chamberlainianum forma *primulinum* var. *flavescens*
Taxonomy as used by J. A. Fowlie in *Orchid Digest*.

P. victoria-regina
P. victoria-regina subsp. *chamberlainianum*
P. victoria-regina subsp. *glaucophyllum*
P. victoria-regina subsp. *glaucophyllum* var. *moquetteanum*
P. victoria-regina subsp. *liemianum*
P. victoria-regina subsp. *primulinum*
P. victoria-regina subsp. *primulinum* forma *purpurascens*
Taxonomy as used by M. W. Wood in *Orchid Review*.

Subgenus *Otopedilum*. Section VIII *Stictopetalum*
From the Greek word, *stiktos*, meaning 'punctured', this name describes the fine, sliver-like hairs which cover the petal surfaces of the members of this section:
P. esquirolei
P. hirsutissimum
P. barbigerum

Subgenus *Otopedilum*. Section IX *Neuropetalum*
From the Greek word, *neuron*, meaning 'nerved', this name refers to the distinctive 'nerved' pattern of veins which the petals of members of this section bear. The leaves of this section are not tessellated:
P. affine
P. boxalli
P. charlesworthii
P. exul
P. gratrixianum
P. insigne
P. villosum

Subgenus *Otopedilum*. Section X *Thiopetalum*
From the Greek word, *theion*, meaning 'sulphur', which refers to the sulphur-coloured petals of the sole member of this section:
P. druryi

Subgenus *Otopedilum*. Section XI *Cymatopetalum*
From the Greek word, *kyma*, meaning 'wave', which refers to the wavy petals with undulate margins which distinguish the members of this section:
P. chiwuanum
P. micranthum
P. spicerianum

Subgenus *Otopedilum*. Section XII *Ceratopetalum*
Derived from the Greek word, *keras*, meaning 'horn', this name describes the petals of the sole member of this section. They sweep outwards, downwards, then upwards again, resembling the horns of a buffalo:
P. fairieanum

Subgenus *Otopedilum*. Section XIII *Spathopetalum*
Taken from the Greek word for 'spatula', describing the flat and 'knife-blade' tipped petals which distinguish this section:
P. amabile
P. appletonianum
P. bullenianum
P. celebesensis
P. linii
P. johorensis
P. robinsonii
P. wolterianum

Subgenus *Otopedilum*. Section XIV *Blepharopetalum*
From the Greek word, *blepharis*, meaning 'eye-lash', describing the fine eye-lash-like hairs which adorn the petal margins of this section:
P. bougainvilleanum
P. dayanum
P. javanicum

P. nigritum
P. papuanum
P. purpuratum
P. purpurascens
P. tonsum
P. violascens
P. virens

Subgenus *Otopedilum*. Section XV *Phacopetalum*
This Greek word describes the warts on the petals of the species comprising this section:
P. argus
P. acmodontum
P. barbatum
P. callosum
P. ciliolare
P. fowliei
P. thailandense
P. schmidtianum
P. urbanianum
P. curtisii
P. hennisianum
P. lawrenceanum
P. sublaeve (O.D.)
P. superbiens

New Sections as Regrouped by the *Orchid Digest*, 1981
Section XVI *Mastersianum* Fowl.
Petals spatulate with small, fine, marginal hairs unlike members of the *Blepharopetalum* section: warts, when present, are small and limited to the basal upper half of the petals; staminode strongly crescent-shaped with a dorsal medial indentation; foliage tessellated. Members of this section were once placed in the *Blepharopetalum* section, but form a natural group:
P. mastersianum

P. wentworthianum
P. zieckianum

Section XVII *Hookerae* Fowl.
Petals knife- or blade-shaped as in *Spathopetalum*; staminode crescent-shaped; this represents a new section with species previously classified within the *Spathopetalum* section:
P. hookerae
P. volonteanum

Section XVIII *Venustum* Fowl.
A natural group of species having marbled foliage, similar petals, and variegated pouches with similar dorsals. Named the section *Venustum* after the first of the species named, these species were formerly included within the *Spathopetalum* Section:
P. venustum
P. wardii
P. sukhakulii

Here is an extract from an article printed in the December 1981 issue of the *Australian Orchid Review*:

> Among much other business conducted at its Seventh Plenary Session in Durban in September 1981, the International Orchid Commission adopted a number of recommendations of its Taxonomy and Nomenclature Committee relating to the botanically correct and (where different) horticulturally recommended names of certain orchid species for future use. Bulletin editors are invited to copy.
>
> The T.N.C. recommended that the following cases of conspecificity be resolved as indicated, for the purposes of which name in future is to be treated as the botanically correct name, which name (if different) is to be treated – or continue to be treated – as the horticulturally recommended name (under the principles set out in Part VI of the *Handbook on Orchid Nomenclature and Registration*, 2nd Edition, 1976), and which name(s) shall be treated as synonyms both botanically and horticulturally:

Paphiopedilums
praestans: to continue in horticultural (including registration) use but in future as a horticulturally recommended name, for the species now correctly known as *glanduliferum*. (Bot./hort. synonyms – *gardineri*; *wilhelminiae*.)
philippinense: to continue in horticultural use as the botanically correct name. (Bot./hort. synonyms – *laevigatum*; *roebelinii*; *Cypripedium cannartianum*).
superbiens: to continue in horticultural use as the botanically correct name. In future, whilst *ciliolare* and *curtisii* are to be treated botanically as synonyms of *superbiens*, both *ciliolare* and *curtisii* continue to be treated as specifically distinct for horticultural, including registration purposes, in the status of equal horticulturally recommended names (in view of their existing substantial involvement in registration as parents over many years).
victoria-regina: to continue in horticultural use as the botanically correct name (Bot./hort. synonym – *victoria-mariae*). Whilst *chamberlainianum*, *glaucophyllum*, and *primulinum* should now be treated botanically as being within *victoria-regina*, they nevertheless all continue to be treated as specifically distinct for horticultural, including registration, purposes, in view of their past substantial use as parents in registration.

THE FORERUNNERS

Although *Paphiopedilum* orchids were introduced to Western culture early in the nineteenth century, they were not the first genus to be cultivated in England. *Bletia purpurea* was imported and successfully grown by an English gardener in 1731. *Phaius tancarvilliae* and *Cymbidium ensifolium* both arrived in 1778 and these were followed by *Epidendrum cochleatum* in 1787 and *Epidendrum fragrans* in 1788.

By 1794, 15 species were in cultivation at Kew. The numbers escalated rapidly when a craze swept through England and the Continent and wealthy horticulturists offered huge prices for the privilege of owning newly discovered species. Plants were collected in the hundreds of thousands and competition became intense between collectors, who jealously kept the true location of their 'finds' secret. More commonly, they gave false locations in order to throw their rivals off the scent. Thus one often reads that a certain species is no longer found in its originally reported locality. It is also possibly the reason why several so called 'lost' species have been re-discovered in a completely new locality.

The first *Paphiopedilum* species were discovered when the orchid craze was at its height. The first to be cultivated was *P. venustum*, which was flowered in England by Veitch in 1819. *P. insigne* arrived in 1819 and first flowered in 1820. *P. javanicum* followed in 1823 and *P. purpuratum* arrived from Hong Kong in 1837. *P. barbatum*, although reaching Messrs Loddige's nursery in 1838, did not flower until 1841. Interest was now at its peak among prominent growers who paid large sums of money for new discoveries by their collectors. *P. lowii* was under cultivation by 1846, closely followed by *P. praestans* and *P. glanduliferum* in 1848, *P. hirsutissimum* in 1857, *P. virens* in 1858,

P. concolor in 1859, and *P. dayanum* and *P. stonei* in 1860.

Like other leading orchid growers of the era, arch-rivals Frederick Sander and James Veitch went to great lengths to preserve the secrecy of their sources, and some of the ruses they employed to find other collectors' sources make interesting reading. The following anecdote described by Waters and Waters illustrates their dedication:

In 1878, a new species flowered among a batch of newly established *P. insigne* in the greenhouse of Lady Spicer. This plant was later to be named *P. spicerianum* in her honour. When news of this exciting new species reached the astute Mr James Veitch, he hastened to call upon Lady Spicer. Before leaving her home that day he had purchased the plant for 70 guineas! He subsequently divided it and sold individual growths for the equivalent of several thousand dollars.

Meanwhile, his rival, Frederick Sander, was not idle! He called upon Lady Spicer, and while taking tea with her, elicited the valuable information that her son was a tea planter in India. Sander took his leave of her (one can well imagine him urging his coachman to greater speeds when out of sight of Lady Spicer's stately home!) and immediately dispatched his ace collector, Mr Forstermann, to visit Lady Spicer's son in India. On meeting Mr Spicer, Forstermann discreetly and cleverly induced him to reveal the habitat of the new species without revealing his identity as a collector. Within a very short time, a consignment of *P. spicerianum*, numbering 40,000 plants, was sent back to England to be auctioned by Frederick Sander. Needless to say, prices of this species then dropped sharply.

Considering the slow passages of sailing ships bringing such consignments to England, it is remarkable that so many plants survived the journey. When they reached their destination they were subjected to conditions of growing which, due to the lack of cultural knowledge prevailing at the time, reduced their numbers even more. They were grown in 'stove-houses' which deprived them of air circulation, subjected them to stifling heat, and kept them saturated with moisture. However, as the years passed, the growers' expertise rapidly increased, their plants began to flourish under improved growing conditions, and they began to hybridise and experiment with seed raising.

Here is a list of the first *Paphiopedilum* hybrids made and successfully grown in England:

Hybrid	Parentage	Registrant	Year
P. Harrisianum	*P. villosum* *P. barbatum*	Veitch	1869
P. Vexillarium	*P. barbatum* *P. fairieanum*	Veitch	1870
P. Arthurianum	*P. fairieanum* *P. insigne*	Sander	1873
P. Euryandrum	*P. barbatum* *P. stonei*	Veitch	1875
P. Selligerum	*P. barbatum* *P. philippinense*	Veitch	1878
P. Morganiae	*P. stonei* *P. superbiens*	Veitch	1880
P. Microchilum	*P. druryi* *P. niveum*	Veitch	1882
P. Leeanum	*P. insigne* *P. spicerianum*	Lawrence	1884
P. Io	*P. argus* *P. lawrenceanum*	Cookson	1886
P. A. de Lairesse	*P. curtisii* *P. rothschildianum*	Sander	1895

In all, 475 *Paphiopedilum* hybrids were made between 1870 and 1900. Many of them are still being grown throughout the world and several are still being used in modern hybridisation.

It is remarkable how successful were their early efforts considering that they were not yet aware of an orchid seed's dependence on a symbiotic relationship with the root fungus (mycorrhiza) for germination.

The first seriously planned sowing of orchid seeds was carried out in

England in 1856 by a Mr Domin, head gardener for James Veitch. After many years of unsuccessful attempts to germinate orchid seeds, he came upon the idea of sowing them on the surface compost of the pod-bearing plant. It was then discovered that the rate of germination increased when pieces of cut roots belonging to the same genus were added to the sowing area.

French botanist Noel Bernard saw that the seeds could only germinate if the root fungus was present. He published a report of his discoveries in 1904, while a German botanist, Professor Burgoff, then unaware of Bernard's results, was also successful in this field and further concluded that different species of orchid fungus existed.

It was not until 1922 that the American botanist Lewis Knudson published the results of his experiments which showed that orchid seeds could be germinated without the presence of root fungus. So was finally introduced the asymbiotic method of seed growing which is used so widely today – growing seeds in a sterile flask on the surface of an agar-based jelly, containing all required nutrients and using various sugars to replace the symbiotic fungus.

CULTURE

With the exception of a few epiphytic and lithophytic species, the majority of the genus are terrestrial in their growth habit. Their home is the shaded dampness of the forest floor or leaf-mould filled rock crevices in areas where high humidity and rainfall ensure that their root systems always remain moist.

The word 'moist' may well be the key word to the successful culture of this genus, and it must be clearly understood that there is a vast difference in meaning between the words 'moist' and 'wet'. Under cultivation, efficient drainage is of prime importance, as no other factor will impede healthy growth as will wet and soggy roots. Pots must have adequate drainage holes, and a layer of coarse charcoal or bark between them and the growing medium will help in keeping them open.

The various merits of terracotta and plastic pots are still the subject of some contention among growers, but during recent years the quality of plastic pots has greatly improved and they are now being used in ever increasing numbers. Among their advantages are lightness, low cost, and ability to remain in one piece when dropped! They are also far less prone to the growth of algae, and, due to their non-porous qualities, dry out far slower thus requiring less frequent watering. Because of this last factor, however, extra care must be taken to ensure that the potting medium is well drained and 'open'. If it is not, 'souring' will occur more rapidly than it would in terracotta pots.

Irrespective of which type of pot is used, the basic requirement of the potting medium is that it retains moisture but not wetness, and that when the plant is watered, excess water will readily escape through the drainage holes.

The potting mixtures used by growers are too numerous to list in these notes. Some contain many and varied components while others, such as straight tan bark and pine bark, often produce good results. A mixture of five parts of fir bark (*Pinus radiata*), two parts of charcoal, and one half part of coarse shell grit, is used by many growers, and produces good results.

In warm temperate areas, if watering is carried out daily during the summer months, I have found the following mixture to be most successful:

1 part coarse shell grit
1 part vermiculite
1 part charcoal
4 parts granulated plastic foam (Isolite)
15 parts 6–12 mm ($\frac{1}{4}$–$\frac{1}{2}$ in) local fir bark.

If daily watering in summer is not possible, the above mixture may be modified by doubling the amount of vermiculite and adding two parts of German peat moss. It will then retain its moisture for a much longer period whilst still retaining its free-draining properties.

When potting, care should be taken that the compost is packed around roots only sufficiently to hold the plant steady. If the plant has insufficient roots to make this possible, it should be securely attached to a small stake until a new root system has formed. Tightly packed compost will prevent efficient drainage and rapid 'souring' and its attendant root-rot will soon follow. Over-potting must be avoided, and, within sensible limits, the smallest pot capable of holding the root system should be used. A plant with a total loss of roots may often be saved by planting in straight sphagnum moss.

The epiphytes, lithophytes, and semi-terrestrials such as *P. lowii, P. parishii, P. randsii, P. philippinense*, and some of the *Cochlopetalum* section, require a much more 'open' growing medium, and larger grades of fir bark and charcoal should be used. Due to their natural manner of growth, they respond well to being suspended in a high and airy section of the glasshouse.

The purely terrestrial members of the genus require a higher humidity, and are often staged upon a moisture-retaining bench. A successful method used by many growers is to cover the bench-tops with a layer of fibrous cement sheeting upon which is a layer of coarse sand topped with a layer of coarse shell grit. If the sand is kept moist, the pots resting upon it will benefit greatly by the extra humidity produced. Another good feature of this type of benching is that the moisture below the pot will induce the roots to grow downwards towards it. When overhead watering is used, the top level of the growing medium tends to retain more moisture than does the lower section of the pot, inducing the roots to grow upwards.

Some growers contend that this method of benching prevents full circulation of air around the pots and can lead to fungoid infection. However, adequate ventilation and a circulating fan will ensure that this possible source of trouble does not eventuate.

As the plants of this genus have no pseudobulbs to maintain a reserve of moisture, it is important that their root system is never allowed to become completely dry. A dehydrated plant will quickly sicken and rapidly lose all resistance to disease. Of most other orchid genera it is true to say that more plants die due to over-watering than to under-watering. However, provided that a free-draining growing medium is used, this old adage does not hold good with the genus *Paphiopedilum*, in fact, the reverse is more likely to be true.

As none of the components of normal potting mediums contain any available plant food, it is advisable to use a fertiliser fortnightly at about half the maker's recommended strength. Immediately the flowering season finishes, a higher nitrogen mixture fertiliser should be used to promote plant growth. Several months before the next flowering season begins, a low nitrogen, high potassium and high phosphorus mixture should be used to initiate flower development.

As well as carrying out a regular feeding programme, a small amount of a slow release fertiliser such as hoof and horn, or blood and bone meal, added to the surface of the growing medium after re-potting will induce a more rapid growth rate. All of the mottled leaf and plain leaf species which grow in limestone areas (especially *P. fairieanum*) respond well to a small amount of dolomite or lime sprinkled on the top of the compost once or twice a year.

With the exception of a few cool growing species such as *P. barbatum*, *P. insigne*, *P. spicerianum*, *P. villosum*, *P. venustum*, and *P. fairieanum*, this genus requires a minimum day temperature of at least 10°C (50°F) for successful culture. Most of the tessellated leaf species and some plain leaf species appreciate an even higher temperature, and if a minimum of 15°C (59°F) can be maintained, then optimum growth will result. Maximum temperatures should not exceed 33°C (90°F), and an evaporative type air cooler is the ideal way of controlling this limit. If the family budget forbids this 'extravagance', then upper and lower ventilators of adequate size, together with a small circulating fan, will help in keeping the maximum temperature down to a reasonable figure. Movement of air is of prime importance in successful culture.

Correct light intensity is a very critical factor in good cultivation. To fully understand its importance, the grower must understand the processes of photosynthesis and osmosis. Obviously, the great majority of growers are familiar with them, but, for the benefit of those who are not, the following brief and very elementary explanation may be of help:

Osmosis: The process whereby moisture in the potting medium (containing various salts and acids in minute amounts) is absorbed by the roots, transmitted through the rhizomes to the leaves, thus reaching the chloroplasts (chlorophyll cells). These cells are situated in the stomata, which are minute pores in the leaf surfaces.

Photosynthesis: During the hours when light is falling on the leaves, the chloroplasts extract carbon from the carbon dioxide present in the atmosphere and combine it with the chlorophyll in the cells. Light falling on the cells reacts with the carbon, chlorophyll, and moisture (from the osmosis process) to form carbohydrates which are essential to all plant life.

During the hours of darkness, this process ceases and oxygen passes through the stomata. This is known as carburising and it has the effect of cleaning out the chloroplasts in readiness for the next period of daylight.

Firstly, it can be seen that unless a healthy root system is present, the process of osmosis cannot function efficiently. Under these conditions no moisture can reach the leaves, thus greatly retarding the process of photosynthesis. Fortunately for those plants having a poor root system, provided they are growing in conditions of reasonable humidity, their leaves may absorb sufficient moisture from the atmosphere to ensure the chloroplasts are supplied.

Secondly, due to the photosynthesis process, it is clear that if insufficient light reaches the plants, their growth rate will be retarded due to a low supply of carbohydrates. As the genus in general is a shade-loving one, many novice growers tend to give their plants excessive shade. The first indication of over-shading is the loss, or partial loss of green pigmentation in the leaves. This is the result of the chlorophyll cells becoming inactive and is a prime cause of the plant losing its resistance to fungus attack. Over-shading is also one of the main causes of an otherwise healthy plant's failure to flower. As such, it may well be that a slight touch of 'sunburn' on the leaves is preferable to the dire results of over-shading. An old 'rule of thumb' states that no shadow should fall on the plant when one's hand is held at a height of 46 cm (18 in) between it and the light source. This may be acceptable as a very rough approximation, but one wonders how much the shading could be reduced yet still cast no shadow? A much more reliable guide is an electronic device now available for less than 10 dollars (Australian) which not only measures light intensity in foot-candles, but also shows pH values and moisture content when its probes are pressed into the potting medium. I have found that a reading of between 400 and 600 foot-candles (4000–6000 lumens per square metre), at noon, gives satisfactory results.

Temperature is also a factor to be considered in the equation of light intensity. The higher the temperature maintained in the glasshouse, the more light is required to maintain the maximum rate of photosynthesis. For optimum growth then, it is necessary to maintain the lowest temperature possible which will suit the plant's needs. As with shading, it may well be a matter of trial and error to arrive at the most suitable figure.

To boost the rate of the photosynthesis process, some growers use the following methods:

1. Horticultural fluorescent tubes (Gro-Lux) are fitted at a height of about half a metre (20 in) above the plants and used to either increase the available daylight or to extend the daylight hours. They are usually used for periods of from 12 to 16 hours a day.

2. L.P. gas (such as Porta-Gas) is burnt in the glasshouse, not as a source of heat, but to increase the amount of carbon dioxide in the air. Unlike coal gas, which gives off carbon monoxide when burnt, L.P. gas gives off carbon dioxide. It is important, however, that the gas be allowed to burn continuously, as a gas harmful to plant life, ethylene, is produced each time the flame is ignited or extinguished.

When using the potting mixture described earlier, it is advisable to re-pot at two-yearly intervals, preferably in early spring after flowering has finished. Provided a plant has at least four or five growths, it may be separated into two pots but it is not advisable to separate a plant into sections of less than two growths. Due to the fine root hairs peculiar to this genus, care must be taken to treat them as gently as possible. Shake off any old compost remaining on them and cut off any dead or damaged roots. As mentioned earlier, do not press the new potting medium tightly around the roots.

If it is wished to grow the plant into a large specimen, it may simply be placed into a new pot large enough to accommodate two years' future growth. When settled into its new home, the rhizome between the new growth and the growth which has just finished flowering may be severed and the cut sprinkled with sulphur. This will induce formation of a new growth and, if the process is repeated each year, will soon produce a large plant.

In retrospect, I believe the factor of greatest importance in successful culture is good air circulation. If it is not complied with even ideal conditions of shading, temperature, watering and feeding will not prevent unhealthy plants and the resultant fungus infection and bud-rot.

PROPAGATION

Once the oldest growth of a large plant has flowered, the rhizome between it and the next growth may be severed. Left undisturbed the old growth will then produce a new growth from a dormant 'eye'. When re-potted the following year, this growth will be mature with its own root system and can be left in the same pot to grow into a larger plant, while the leading growths are removed and re-potted. It is strongly advisable not to break the plant into less than two growth sections. Unfortunately, however, some species have the habit of breaking up into single growths once disturbed, leaving the grower with no option but to re-pot as single growths. Care must be taken to avoid damaging the root hairs peculiar to this genus. Merely cut off any dead or damaged roots and use a pot just large enough to accommodate one year's growth. Do not ram the compost tightly as this may impede the free drainage so necessary for good culture.

Vegetative propagation such as described above is adequate enough to supply the grower with a few spare plants for himself or friends. However, if supplies of all species are to be maintained in such numbers as to supply the needs of the rapidly increasing numbers of growers, then propagation by seed is essential. Many countries have already banned the export of their indigenous species and some previously fairly common species such as *P. purpuratum* have become extinct in nature as the result of indiscriminate collecting. It is obvious that if preservation of the species is to be achieved, then a programme of seed propagation is essential.

Propagation from Seed
Pollination is achieved by transferring pollen from the anthers to the stigmatic

surface by means of a toothpick or similar object. Within a few days the flower will wither, the ovary begin to swell, and the seed pod form. Ripening takes from nine to 12 months and the pod must be watched carefully towards the end of this period. As soon as it shows signs of beginning to split, it should be harvested and placed in a clean envelope. If green pod culture is desired, the pod must be harvested no later than 6 months after pollination. (This applies to species only, as hybrids take longer to reach the stage necessary for germination.)

The earliest method of seed raising, known as the symbiotic method, is no longer widely used due to its very low (10 per cent) germination rate. It involved sprinkling mature seed on the compost surface of a host plant and lightly spraying with water. The host plant need not be of the same species as the seed but early records indicate that the germination rate was higher if this was so. The advantage of this method is that the seed need not be sterilised but great care must be taken when watering so that the minute seeds are not washed away.

The modern method, or asymbiotic method, entails sowing the sterilised seed on the surface of a sterilised agar jelly medium containing both organic and inorganic nutrients, the whole being protected in a sterilised glass flask.

This method, commonly known as 'flasking', is a rather involved one which requires more than a little skill and a considerable amount of equipment. Unless you intend to produce seedlings on a very large scale, I strongly advise utilising the services of one of the many commercial laboratories which advertise in orchid periodicals. Their charges are nominal and their success rate practically 100 per cent. Many an enthusiastic grower (including myself!) has spent a considerable amount of money on the necessary equipment and chemicals, 'selfed' his rare and cherished plant, flasked the resulting seed, only to find that the plant died after the effort of producing the seed pod, and that all the flasks succumbed to infection. However, if you are anxious to try your hand at the process, you will find many orchid books available which deal with the subject in much greater depth than is possible here.

Irrespective of the origin of the flask, there finally comes the time to 'de-flask'. This process may well be likened to that of human birth – a sudden and traumatic transition from the 'womb' of the flask to the 'cot' of the community pot – from the sterile agar containing all required nutriment, maintained at an ideal temperature and receiving optimum light intensity, to the harsh outside world. A world of varying temperature, humidity and light, where fungoid infections and voracious predators lie in wait, and where nutrition must be obtained from outside sources.

The following method which I have used has proved highly successful, and may be of help to the novice grower:

One of the greatest killers of young seedlings is dehydration due to transpiration, i.e. loss of moisture by evaporation through the leaves. To reduce the chances of this happening, de-flasking is carried out at the end of winter so that the plantlets will be reasonably advanced before the onset of hot weather. Provided that the room in which the seedlings are to be grown is small, the cost of heating it during the colder months will be minimal, vastly less than would be the cost of cooling it during summer.

Now that the time and place of the process have been decided upon, one must consider the actual act of birth. Will it be:

A. A 'natural' birth entailing removal of the flask stopper and drawing the plantlets out by means of a bent wire or long handled spoon or,

B. A 'Caesarean' birth in which the bottom of the flask is removed and the mass of agar and seedlings removed intact?

In my opinion, the first method has only one advantage! It saves the cost of the flask, about 50 cents! Surely a poor return considering that the mass of plantlets will be broken up and that many tiny leaves and roots will be damaged.

Hopefully, method 'B' will be adopted, and the flask will be wrapped in newspaper and its flat bottom surface tapped gently with a small hammer until it shatters. The pad of agar and seedlings may then be removed intact, taking care to avoid fragments of glass.

The next step is to immerse the mass of plantlets and agar in a basin containing a solution of propamocarb and water for about 10 minutes. This chemical is now available under the trade name of Previcur. Solution strength should be only 3 ml (about a teaspoon) to 2 L ($3\frac{1}{2}$ pints) of water. It is 100 per cent effective in controlling pithium (damping-off), previously the greatest cause of seedling loss. It also controls phytophthora (root-rot diseases), and downy mildews. As an added bonus it also greatly assists plant growth. After gentle agitation to remove all traces of agar jelly, the pad of seedlings is ready to be placed in its community pot. A 100 mm (4 in) plastic pot is used, crocked with coarse charcoal, and filled loosely with a mixture of 1 part fine fir bark, 1 part fine charcoal, 1 part fine shell grit, and 1 part live sphagnum moss rubbed through a 5 mm ($\frac{1}{4}$ in) sieve. Once prepared, the pot of compost is soaked for several hours in the same Previcur solution. The pad of seedlings is then placed on top of the compost and gently pressed down so that some of the compost will find its way between the roots. It is then placed above a source of warmth on a layer of sand topped with shell grit, the moist sand to maintain a high humidity, and the shell grit to deter snails and slugs. Bottom heat, although possibly not essential, greatly increases the growth rate. I use a homemade device which utilises only one 40 watt lamp and is most economical to make and operate, accommodating up to 20 pots.

For optimum growth the seedlings are grown under horticultural fluorescent lamps. The newer type of long wave tubes are used for a period of 14 hours each day and are placed 40 cm (16 in) above the plants.

The plants are sprayed daily with rain water, the inconvenience of collecting and storing it being greatly outweighed by the dramatic increase in growth rate attained. It appears that while fluoride may be beneficial to human teeth, it is not appreciated by orchid seedlings!

Fertilising is not carried out until three weeks after de-flasking, after which time a solution of fairly high nitrogen content fertiliser is applied weekly at one-third recommended strength.

The great majority of orchid culture books advise that the seedlings should remain in their community pots for a period of up to one year or until they grow their 'new' roots as distinct from their 'agar' roots. However, I have achieved better results by leaving them in their community pots for only about six weeks, just long enough for them to become used to conditions outside the flask, and for their leaves to harden slightly. The mass of plantlets is then gently disentangled and they are individually potted into 50 mm (2 in) tubes using the same potting medium, and drenching again in a Previcur solution.

When healthy roots have formed and the leaves have reached a span of about 80 mm (3 in), the plants are re-potted into 80 mm (3 in) square pots, this time using the coarser potting medium described in the cultural section (page 19). At this stage they no longer require bottom heat or artificial lighting, and may be transferred to normal glasshouse conditions.

PESTS AND DISEASES

Apart from a chance fungus infection which can strike one or more plants in a collection, seemingly without any reason, the grower of this genus is fortunate that it is normally free from many of the pests and diseases which plague most other genera. This is true only if the grower ensures that his glasshouse is kept clean and well screened, and that no plants are admitted to it until they are proven to be clean and free from disease.

Snails and slugs: Although the glasshouse should be screened against entry of these pests, any of the commercial snail baits such as Defender will take care of stray intruders. It should be remembered that almost all snail baits contain metaldehyde, which is attractive to dogs and fatal to them if eaten.

Bush snails: These tiny but voracious snails, with their distinctive odour of garlic, can cause great damage to the root system of all orchids. Being strictly nocturnal and lurking within the crevices of the potting medium, they may remain undetected for a long period and cannot be controlled by any of the commercial snail baits. Some years ago the *Orchid Digest* published a very effective method of controlling these pests which produces a 100 per cent kill rate:

> Dissolve one tablespoon of metaldehyde powder and one tablespoon of washing soda in one pint of boiling water. Add this mixture to four gallons of cold water, then completely immerse each pot in the solution until the compost is saturated.
> [One pint equals 568 millilitres, four gallons equals 18 litres.]

Slaters: Another root-destroying pest which can cause great damage if not quickly detected and controlled. Fortunately slaters are easily eradicated by saturating each pot with a solution of one tablespoon of Lane's Wellspray to five litres (about eight pints) of water. This mixture is also very effective in the control of aphids, scale, and mealy bug. For even greater control of the last two pests, some soluble white oil should be added in accordance with the maker's recommended dosage.

Fungus infections: Regular sprayings with a good fungicide at three-monthly intervals will help in preventing fungoid infections. Any of the commercial preparations such as Phaltan, Zineb, or Natriphene are effective. A new preparation recently released, Previcur, is giving good results in the control of Erwina rot (soft brown rot). When using any horticultural chemicals it is most important that the maker's safety instructions are heeded. Skin contact or inhalation may be highly dangerous and it is advisable to use a respirator and goggles when spraying.

If overhead watering is used, care must be taken to ensure that water is not allowed to lie in the leaf axils, especially during the period when buds are beginning to form. If this is allowed to happen, fungus infection will be encouraged and the rapid rotting-off of buds will soon follow. An extra application of fungicide at this time will help to reduce bud loss, but the best 'preventive medicine' of all is the supply of adequate air circulation and taking care that water is not allowed to lie in the leaf axils.

The
Tropical Asiatic
Slipper Orchids

P. acmodontum Schoser ex Wood 1977

Subgenus *Otopedilum*. Section XV *Phacopetalum*
Philippines: Visayan area.

Leaves are broadly ovate, light green tessellated with darker green, about 12 cm (5 in) long and 4 cm ($1\frac{1}{2}$ in) wide.

The flower scape is up to 20 cm (8 in) tall and bears one, or rarely two flowers. It is greenish-purple and densely pubescent.

The dorsal sepal is white, shaded basally with rose-pink except for the central section which is a light apple-green. It bears about 10 dark purplish-green vertical veins, and has ciliate margins.

Petals are bright green basally, changing to a rich pinkish-rose at about mid-length. Dark green veins extend from the base almost to the apex and the margins are ciliate. Above the mid-line, the green basal colouring is darker. Dark brown spots are scattered over the mid-section, and the upper margin is slightly undulate.

The lip is brownish-yellow suffused with green. The infolded side lobes meet and are whitish-green, with scattered rose-red spots.

Ventral sepal is less than half the size of the dorsal but has similar colouring and markings.

The staminode is cordate and brown, with creamish-white vertical centre line and margins.

Flowers in late spring.
Warm conditions.

P. adductum Asher 1983

Subgenus *Anotopedilum*. Section III *Coryopedilum*
Philippine Is., Mindanao.

This 'lost' species was re-discovered in 1980. Its leaves are bright green, untessellated, 30 to 45 cm (12 to $17\frac{3}{4}$ in) long, and 3.5 to 4.5 cm ($1\frac{1}{2}$ to $1\frac{3}{4}$ in) wide.

The flower scape is stout, spotted with purple, over 30 cm (12 in) in height, and bears two to five flowers.

The dorsal sepal is about 6 cm ($2\frac{1}{2}$ in) long and 4.5 cm ($1\frac{3}{4}$ in) wide, acutely pointed and 'pinched' at the apex. It is ivory-white in colour and bears about 15 vertical dark crimson lines of varying length.

The petals are very narrow and elongated, white, and marked basally with small crimson blotches which merge into about four narrow striations which extend to the tips. The upper margins are basally undulate and ciliate.

The pouch is similar to that of *P. stonei* in colour and shape. It is ivory-white, delicately veined and tinted with deep rose.

The synsepalum is smaller than the

dorsal sepal but similar in shape and colouring.

The staminode is narrow and curved under as in *P. rothschildianum*, hirsute and markedly bifid at the apex.

Flowers in summer.

Warm conditions.

P. affine De Wildem. 1906

Subgenus *Otopedilum*. Section IX *Neuropetalum*
Southern China, Tonkin.

Leaves linear-oblong, 15 cm (6 in) long and 3 cm ($1\frac{1}{4}$ in) wide, slightly tessellated on upper surface and with bi-dentate tips.

The flower scape is about 15 cm (6 in) long, pubescent, green, slightly streaked with purple.

The bracts are slightly less than half the size of the ovary, green, striped with crimson basally, glabrous, with ciliate margins.

The dorsal sepal is ovate, 5 cm (2 in) high and 2.8 cm ($1\frac{1}{8}$ in) wide, with margins rolled backwards. Green from base to mid-height, then white to apex; striped with green, and speckled with violet on lower third.

The petals are spatulate, 6 cm ($2\frac{3}{8}$ in) long and 2.3 cm ($\frac{7}{8}$ in) wide, green flushed with light violet, glabrous, and with ciliate margins. Synsepalum is broadly ovate, shorter than the dorsal sepal, margins reflexed basally, glabrous on front surface, and bearing white hairs on back surface.

The labellum is about 4.3 cm ($1\frac{3}{4}$ in) long, green washed with light violet.

The staminode has a tri-dentate lower margin.

P. amabile Hallier 1895

Subgenus *Otopedilum*. Section XIII *Spathopetalum* (*Cyp. amabile* Hallier f.)
West Borneo: near Sintang. (Re-discovered 1979.)

Leaves are dark green tessellated with lighter green, 15 cm (6 in) long and 3 cm ($1\frac{1}{4}$ in) wide.

The flower scape is up to 30 cm (12 in) tall, bearing a single flower which closely resembles *P. bullenianum* but differs in the shape of its staminode.

The dorsal sepal is green, lightening to white at the apex. Basally, it bears a narrow, white, transverse band surmounted by a narrow, reddish band.

Petals are greenish-yellow towards the base, changing to reddish-brown except along the margins, which bear a few scattered dark-brown warts. Basally, the upper margin is undulate and sparsely haired.

The lip is greenish basally, changing to brownish-red towards the aperture which has a narrow green margin.

Ventral sepal is smaller than the dorsal but similar in colour.

The staminode is oval, light green with a white centre and margin. It has a deep and narrow lower incisure which forms two in-pointing lateral lobes.

Flowers in spring and early summer.

Warm conditions.

P. x *ang-thong* Fowl., *nat. hybd.* 1980 (O.D.)

Subgenus *Brachypetalum*
Northern islands of Ang-Thong Archipelago.

Following an article by Kohji Karasawa published in the *Bulletin of the Hiroshima Botanical Gardens*, March 1979, American orchidists now consider this orchid to be one of a natural 'swarm' of *P. godefroyae* and *P. niveum*.

Found growing at low elevations in crevices of limestone outcrops.

Leaves are 8 to 13 cm (3 to 5 in) long and 3 to 4 cm ($1\frac{1}{4}$ to $1\frac{1}{2}$ in) wide. Deep green, tessellated with light greyish-green, and spotted with purple on undersides.

The scape is 10 to 12 cm (4 to 5 in) long and bears one or two flowers.

Dorsal sepal is about 3 cm (1 in) wide, broadly ovate, satin-white with large reddish-purple spots. It is slightly flushed with yellowish-green at mid-vein.

Petals are widely rounded and of the same colouring as the dorsal sepal.

The lip is egg-shaped with the same colouring as the other segments but having much finer spotting.

The ventral sepal is smaller than the dorsal, much narrower, with same basic colouring, but stained with light green on back surface.

The staminode is cordate (heart-shaped) with the same colouring and markings as the lip. It bears a bright yellow mark in its centre.

Flowers in summer and autumn.

Warm conditions.

P. *appletonianum* (Gower) Rolfe 1893

Subgenus *Otopedilum*. Section XIII *Spathopetalum* 2n = 38 (*Cyp. appletonianum* Gower)
Himalayas, Assam, Thailand, south-west Laos.

Leaves are strap-shaped, keeled, light to medium green, faintly tessellated, and streaked with purple on their undersides.

The flower scape is up to 42 cm

(16 in) tall, brownish, hirsute, and bears a single flower.

Dorsal sepal is small but broad, tapering to an acute point, yellowish-green, striped with brown basally, hooded, and with re-curved basal margins.

The petals are spreading, very slightly drooping, or sometimes horizontal. Twisted, with undulate upper margins. Greenish basally, widening and turning to a pale rose-red towards the tips. Scattered dark brown spots are borne basally on the upper margins, with a few single, dark hairs.

The lip is pinkish-fawn, lightening towards the 'toe', with a green margin around the aperture. It is long, narrow, and pointed at the toe. The interior is profusely spotted with purple.

Ventral sepal is apple-green, keeled, and narrow.

The staminode is green, vertically ovate, with a deep lower incisure having mesially directed (inwards pointing) lateral lobes.

Flowers in winter.

Intermediate conditions.

As this species is very similar to *P. wolterianum*, the distinguishing features of both species are listed below:

P. appletonianum
Leaves light green and faintly tessellated.

Flower scape up to 42 cm (16 in) tall.
Petals horizontal or very slightly drooping. Twisted.
Staminode vertically ovate with deep lower incisure having its lobes directed inwards.

P. wolterianum
Leaves dark green and prominently tessellated.
Flower scape up to 50 cm (20 in) tall.
Petals drooping to 45 degrees and untwisted.
Staminode horizontally oval with shallow lower incisure having its lateral lobes directed outwards.

P. argus (Rchb.f.) Stein 1873

Subgenus *Otopedilum*. Section *Phacopetalum* 2n = 38 (*Cyp. argus* Rchb.f., *Cyp. barbatum* var. *argus* Vos., *Cyp. pitcherianum* Manda, *Cordula argus* Rolfe) Philippines: Luzon, Negros.

Found growing at elevations of 700 to 3000 metres (2300 to 9800 feet).

Leaves up to 20 cm (8 in) long and 3 cm (1 in) wide. Dark green tessellated with yellowish-green on upper surfaces. Undersides are pale green and untessellated.

The flower scape is up to 30 cm (12 in) tall and bears a single flower.

The dorsal sepal is large, broadly ovate basally, and tapering to an acute apex. It is white with green striations and a few short purplish lines basally.

Petals are up to 6 cm ($2\frac{1}{2}$ in) long, twisted, undulate on margins, and turning shaply downwards. Basally, they are white with green veins, turning to a light rose-purple towards the tips. They are spotted all over with blackish-purple, and bear purplish hairs on both margins.

The lip is broad, dark purplish-brown with paler underside veined with dark green, and densely spotted inside with reddish-purple.

Ventral sepal is smaller than the dorsal, white with green veining.

Flowers in early spring.

Warm conditions.

P. armeniacum Chen & Liu 1982

Subgenus *Brachypetalum* 2n = 26
China: Bijiang, Southern Yunnan.

A newly discovered species of epiphytic habit, having an elongated rhizome 2 to 3 mm in diameter.

Leaves are five to seven in number, oblong, 6 to 12 cm ($2\frac{1}{2}$ to 5 in) long and 1.8 to 2.3 cm ($\frac{3}{4}$ in to $\frac{7}{8}$ in) wide. Apices are acute, the upper surfaces bearing distinctive white tessella-tions. Undersides are keeled and densely spotted with purple.

The flower scape is erect, sometimes slightly bent, 24 to 26 cm ($9\frac{1}{2}$ to 10 in) tall, green with purplish blotches, and clothed with brownish hairs. There is a single, golden yellow flower.

The dorsal sepal is lanceolate, oval, 2.2 to 4.8 cm ($\frac{7}{8}$ to 2 in) long, and 1.4 to 2.2 cm ($\frac{1}{2}$ to $\frac{7}{8}$ in) wide. The apex is pointed, front surface glabrous, and the rear surface is almost completely clothed with fine hairs. The margin is ciliate; the segment bears 11 to 13 vertical veins.

The synsepalum is similar in shape and colour but is slightly smaller: 2 to 2.5 cm ($\frac{3}{4}$ to 1 in) wide with an obtuse apex. The front surface is glabrous and rear surface hirsute.

The petals are large, broadly ovate, almost rounded: 2.8 to 5.3 cm (1 to $2\frac{1}{4}$ in) long and 2.5 to 3 cm (1 to $1\frac{1}{4}$ in) wide, bearing 11 to 19 nerves. The bases of the front surfaces are clothed with whitish hairs, and the rear surface is glabrous. Both margins are ciliate.

The labellum is elliptically egg-shaped, 4 to 5 cm ($1\frac{5}{8}$ to 2 in) long and 3.5 to 4 cm ($1\frac{1}{2}$ to $1\frac{5}{8}$ in) wide. Aperture margins are closely in-rolled, the inner surface is purple spotted and clothed basally with whitish hairs.

The staminode is broadly ovate, 1 to 2 cm ($\frac{3}{8}$ to $\frac{3}{4}$ in) long and 1 to 1.5

cm ($\frac{3}{8}$ to $\frac{5}{8}$ in) wide with the apex hooked and bent forward. Golden yellow spotted with brown; rear surface is keeled.

The ovary is green, hexagonal–cylindrical, bearing whitish hairs.

Flowering season not known.

Intermediate conditions.

An article by P. J. Cribb and C. Z. Tang in the *Orchid Review* of May 1983 suggests that this species may eventually prove to be a colour variant of *P. delenatii*.

P. barbatum (Lindl.) Stein 1841

Subgenus *Otopedilum*. Section XV *Phacopetalum* 2n = 38 (*Cyp. barbatum* Lindl., *Cordula barbata* Rolfe)
Mt Ophir, Sumatra; Thailand; Malay Peninsula.

Favouring crevices containing moss and decaying leaves, this species grows in shaded valleys on granite rocks at elevations of 1000 metres (about 3300 feet).

Leaves are 10 to 15 cm (4 to 6 in) long, pointed and channelled, light green tessellated with darker green.

The flower scape is up to 35 cm (14 in) tall and bears one, or rarely two flowers.

The dorsal sepal is large and broad, almost circular, and slightly keeled. Greenish-white shading to pale green basally, stained with purple in centre section, and having a wide white margin. Its vertical stripes are green basally, changing to purple as they near the apex.

Petals are narrow, spreading, and slightly drooping. Greenish-white, turning to purple apically. Both margins are ciliate and bear small blackish warts.

The lip is large, almost as long as the petals, deep purple frontally and turning paler towards the rear. Side lobes are rosy-purple, densely spotted with purplish-crimson.

Ventral sepal is much smaller than the dorsal but of similar colouring.

The staminode is whitish-green with dark green markings in central section. The lower margin is widely incised, forming two prominent 'horns'.

Flowers in spring.

Warm conditions.

P. barbigerum Tang & Wang 1940

Subgenus *Otopedilum*. Section VIII *Stictopetalum*
China: Kweichow.

I am extremely grateful to Professor Wu Zhengyi, Director of the Kunming Institute of Botany, for supplying the Latin description from which this greatly condensed description was taken.

This species is found growing together with *P. esquirolei* in Kweichow province, and both species are closely related and similar in appearance. *P. barbigerum*, however, has smaller flowers and bears a distinctive tuft of hairs at the base of each petal.

It is an upright plant of terrestrial habit, 15 to 20 cm (6 to 8 in) high, with a very short rhizome. The root system is very small, and the roots are thick and hairy.

Leaves are nine or 10 in number, linear, strap-like, obtuse, erect, and open in habit. Thin but leathery, smooth on both surfaces, apex somewhat bidentate, and slightly serrulate.

The flower scape is erect, thin, single flowered, densely haired, and 8 to 15 cm (3 to 6 in) tall.

Bracts are ovate and cucullate, obtuse and serrulate, fairly smooth. Ovary is about half the size of the bract.

The flower is about 6 cm ($2\frac{1}{2}$ in) wide. Dorsal sepal almost round but wedge-shaped basally, and with a smooth, rounded apex, bearing about 17 veins 3 cm (1 in) long. Front surface is glabrous, and rear surface hirsute.

Petals are widely spread, prominently undulate, narrow basally, gradually widening towards an obtuse apex. Strap-like, 3 to 4 cm (1 to $1\frac{5}{8}$ in) long and 9 mm ($\frac{3}{8}$ in) wide, both surfaces glabrous except for small but distinctive tufts of hair just above point of attachment. Both margins are sparsely haired.

The pouch is about 3 cm (1 in) long, with outer surfaces smooth, and interior finely haired.

Synsepalum is hirsute on back surface, but the front surface is smooth except for a small area just above the base. Oblong in shape with an obtuse apex, 3.5 cm ($1\frac{3}{8}$ in) long, and 1.5 cm ($\frac{5}{8}$ in) wide, margins finely ciliate.

Column densely ciliate basally.

Staminode is five-angled, and has an acute apex.

Cool conditions.

P. bellatulum (Rchb.f.) Pfitz. 1888

Subgenus *Brachypetalum* 2n = 26 (*Cyp. bellatulum* Rchb.f.)
Burma: Moulmein; Thailand.

Found growing in pockets of decaying vegetation at elevations of 1000 to 1600 metres (3300 to 5300 feet). Although almost always experiencing conditions of high humidity, it is subject to minimum temperatures of as low as 0°C (32°F).

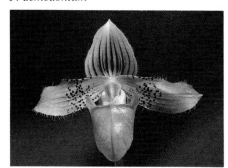

P. acmodontum

P. amabile

P. adductum

P. x *ang-thong*

P. appletonianum

P. argus

P. bellatulum

P. armeniacum

P. barbatum

P. bodegomii

P. bullenianum

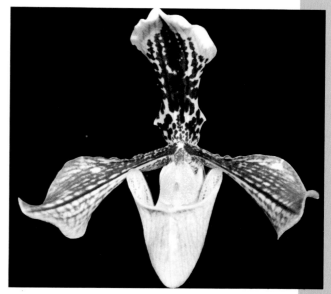

P. bougainvilleanum

P. boxalli

P. callosum

P. celebesensis

P. chamberlainianum

P. chamberlainianum forma *primulinum*
var. *flavescens*

P. chamberlainianum forma *primulinum*
var. *flavum*

P. chamberlainianum subsp. *liemiana*

P. curtisii

P. ciliolare

P. charlesworthii

P. concolor

P. delenatii

P. dayanum

P. druryi

P. dianthum

Leaves are narrowly elliptical, 15 cm (6 in) long and 4 cm (1½ in) wide. The upper surfaces are green, mottled with greyish-green, and the undersides are reddish-purple.

The flower scape is very short, hirsute, and deep purple in colour. It bears a single flower which almost touches the leaves, and is 6 to 10 cm (2½ to 4 in) wide.

The dorsal sepal is round and concave, curving over to form a cup. It is white to creamy-white, sometimes flushed with pink, and fairly uniformly speckled with pinkish to deep purple spots.

Petals are broadly ovate, slightly drooping and almost surround the lip. They are of the same colouring as the dorsal sepal.

The lip is small and daintily shaped. White, with less spotting than the other segments.

Ventral sepal is one-third the size of the dorsal, but similar in shape and colouring.

The staminode is cordate, concave, and notched at the apex. It has finer spotting than the lip, and a small creamish-green central area is completely free of spotting.

Flowers in summer.
Intermediate conditions.

P. bodegomii Hort. 1980 (O.D.)

Subgenus *Anotopedilum*. Section III *Coryopedilum* 2n = 26
Western New Guinea.

Not yet formally described, this new species is found growing in a limestone area in the vicinity of Wissel Lakes, Western New Guinea, at an elevation of 1600 metres (about 5300 feet). It appears to be a high altitude form of *P. praestans* but is only two-thirds the size of the latter.

The petals are much more pendulous and twisted and the lip is more slender and has a pinkish tinge.

The staminodes are different in their manner of incisures.

Warm conditions.

P. bougainvilleanum Schoser ex Fowl. 1971

Subgenus *Otopedilum*. Section XIV *Blepharopetalum* 2n = 40
Bougainville Is. (Solomon Is.)

Found growing in an area where rain falls almost daily and humidity is always over 90 per cent.

Leaves are greyish-green and faintly tessellated, 14 to 20 cm (5½ to 8 in) long and 2 to 4 cm (1 to 1½ in) wide.

The flower scape is 10 to 20 cm (4 to 8 in) tall and bears a single flower.

Dorsal sepal is broad, white, and veined with green. Acutely pointed and slightly hooded at apex. Basal margins are slightly re-flexed.

The petals are drooping, greenish-white basally, shading to rose-purple apically, and bearing closely spaced parallel veins of dark green.

The lip is medium green with olive green veining. The in-folded side lobes are greenish-white.

Ventral sepal is much smaller than the dorsal, but similar in shape and colour.

The staminode is light green with darker green markings, ovoid, with no apical incisure. The lower incisure is wide and forms two rounded lateral horns.

Flowers in spring.
Warm conditions.

P. boxallii (Rchb.f.) Stein 1877

Subgenus *Otopedilum*. Section IX *Neuropetalum* 2n = 26 (*Cyp. boxalli* Rchb.f.) Burma, Malaya.

Sometimes listed as a variety of *P. villosum*, this species is found growing at an elevation of 2000 metres (almost 6600 feet) but is now rarely seen either in cultivation or in its natural habitat.

Leaves are about 24 cm (10 in) long and 3 cm (1 in) wide, fairly stiff, and notched at the tip. Light green on undersides with upper surfaces darker and very faintly mottled with lighter green.

Flower scape is up to 25 cm (10 in) tall, pale green, densely covered with long red hairs. It is usually single flowered, but on rare occasions two flowers may be borne.

The dorsal sepal is about 6 cm ($2\frac{1}{2}$ in) tall and 3 cm (1 in) wide and has undulate upper margins. It is broad at the apex, narrowing and curving backwards as it nears the base. Green, with a wide, white margin, it bears heavy purplish spotting in the form of vertical stripes.

Petals are greenish-yellow, veined with brownish-purple, and drooping at an angle of about 45 degrees. They are narrow basally, widening towards the tips and bear a prominent mid-line of purplish-brown. Below this line the veining is less prominent.

The lip is large and has prominent auricles ('ears'). It is yellow and tinged and veined with dull purple.

The ventral sepal is longer than the dorsal but much narrower. Very light green with about eight vertical rows of purplish-brown spots.

The staminode is oval, pale yellow, and with a prominent green tubercle in the centre.

All segments have a highly glazed

appearance similar to that of *P. villosum*.

Flowers in winter.

Cool conditions.

P. bullenianum (Rchb.f.) Stein 1865

Subgenus *Otopedilum*. Section XIII *Spatho-petalum* 2n = 40 (*Cyp. bullenianum* Rchb.f.)
North Borneo.

A plant of dwarf habit which favours very humid and warm conditions. It is found growing in thick leaf mould in densely shaded positions at an elevation of 500 metres (about 1600 feet).

Leaves are strap-shaped, up to 16 cm (6 in) long and 3 cm (1 in) wide. Pale green with a slight blueish tinge, faintly tessellated, and bearing purple spotting on the basal sections of the undersides.

The flower scape is up to 30 cm (12 in) tall, and bears a single flower about 7 cm (3 in) wide. The flower closely resembles *P. linii* but the latter has no purple markings on the undersides of its leaves.

The dorsal sepal is small and has a prominently hooded apex. Green, with paler green margins and darker vertical striations. A small streak of purple extends from the base to about half the height of the segment.

Petals are spreading, widening, and slightly re-curving towards the tips. Greenish, flushed with purple apically, and bearing purple-brown hairless warts near the basal margins.

The lip is dark, purplish-red lightening towards the 'toe' and with a narrow green margin around the rim. The front centre of the rim bears a very pronounced cleft. The lateral lobes bear large, dark-brown warts.

Ventral sepal is almost as long as the dorsal but much narrower.

The staminode is whitish with green markings. Oval, with its lower incisure much deeper than the upper. A greenish-yellow uvula projects downwards into the lower incisure.

Flowers in summer.

Warm conditions.

P. callosum (Rchb.f.) Stein 1886

Subgenus *Otopedilum*. Section XV *Phaco-petalum* (*Cyp. callosum* Rchb.f.)
Thailand, Cambodia.

Found growing in very moist conditions on the lower slopes of mountains at elevations of 600 to 1200 metres (about 2000 to 4000 feet).

Leaves rather few, up to 22 cm (9 in) long and 4 cm ($1\frac{1}{2}$ in) wide. Light green with dark green tessellation, veined, rigid and having forked tips. The undersides are keeled and marked basally with purple.

The flower scape is up to 40 cm (16 in) tall, hirsute, and bears a single flower 9 cm ($3\frac{1}{2}$ in) wide.

The dorsal sepal is broad and almost circular, with white and slightly undulate margins. The basal one-third of the segment is white, above which is an arching band of rosy-pink. About 20 green veins rise from the base and change to purplish-brown on reaching the pink tinted section.

Petals are wide and bend downwards at an angle of 45 degrees. They are green basally, turning to a rosy-pink towards the tips. Darker green veins run longitudinally and fade out towards the pink section. Both margins are ciliate and the upper margins bears about eight black warts. In some forms these warts appear on both margins and also on the central section.

The lip is wide, rounded, purplish-brown, shading to green at the toe. The in-folded side lobes are marked with rosy-brown dots.

The ventral sepal is narrow, cupped, projecting forward, and striped with green and purple veins.

The staminode is squarish in shape, very light green marbled with dark green and lavender, and has a large central incisure basally which forms two large lateral 'horns'.

Flowers in spring and summer.

Warm conditions.

P. celebesensis Fowl. & Birk. 1980

Subgenus *Otopedilum*. Section XIII *Spathopetalum* 2n = 42
Indonesia: Rantepao, Celebes.

Plant is of dwarf habit, forming a clump with the new growths emerging about 2 cm ($\frac{3}{4}$ in) away from the old growth.

The leaves are only 5 to 6 cm (2 to $2\frac{1}{2}$ in) long and 3 cm (1 in) wide. Deeply keeled and split at the tips, dark green with light green tessellation. The undersides are paler with a very slight purplish flush basally.

The flower scape is about 12 cm (5 in) tall, purplish-red, hirsute, and bearing a single flower.

Dorsal sepal is 2.5 cm (1 in) high and 1.5 cm ($\frac{1}{2}$ in) wide. Triangular in shape, tapering to an acute apex. Margins and tip are in-curved forming a pronounced hood. Medium green with faint darker green vertical striations. The back surface is covered with fine purple down.

Petals are 2.5 cm (1 in) long and 1 cm ($\frac{3}{8}$ in) wide, narrow basally, and widening at mid-length, then narrowing slightly towards the distinctly flattened tips. Both margins are slightly in-rolled. Light green basally, flushing to light pink in central section, then turning to green at the tips. A few rose-pink stripes run horizontally in the mid-section, and about three large blackish-brown spots are borne near the margins.

The lip is very narrow with infolded side-lobes touching. Only 0.5 cm ($\frac{1}{4}$ in) wide and 2 cm ($\frac{3}{4}$ in) long, dull green with pinkish-brown veining and a narrow green margin.

Ventral sepal similar to dorsal but much smaller.

The staminode is rhomboid shaped, light green with a distinctive 'H'-shaped marking of dark green. Its lower margin has a large central incisure which forms two prominent 'horns'.

Flowers in autumn.

Warm conditions.

P. chamberlainianum (O'Brien) Stein 1892 (O.D.)

P. victoria-regina (Sander) M. W. Wood subsp. *chamberlainianum* (Sander) M. W. Wood, *comb. nov.* 1976 (O.R.)

Subgenus *Otopedilum*. Section VII *Cochlopetalum* 2n = 32 (*Cyp. chamberlainianum* Sander)
Central Sumatra.

This species is unusual in that it has been found growing as a terrestrial, an epiphyte, and a lithophyte. Favours brightly lit positions at elevations of 700 to 2000 metres (2300 to 6600 feet).

A very robust plant with bright green strap-shaped leaves, up to 30 cm (12 in) long and 6 cm (2$\frac{1}{2}$ in) wide. They are notched at the tips, sometimes faintly tessellated, and have ciliate basal margins. The undersides are lightly shaded with purple basally but lack deep purple spots or blotches.

The flower scape is stout, straight, and up to 60 cm (24 in) tall. It is hirsute, and bears up to eight flowers progressively over a long period of time. The flowers are up to 8 cm (3 in) wide.

The dorsal sepal is almost circular, white, greenish-brown basally, and bears about six prominent purplish-brown vertical striations. The back surface is hirsute.

Petals are long, twisted, horizontally spreading, and have ciliate and undulate margins. Whitish, with many short, horizontal, purplish markings.

The lip is white around the aperture, blushing to pink and rose basally. It is broadly distended below the middle, and densely spotted with deeper pink.

Ventral sepal is smaller than the dorsal but otherwise similar.

The staminode is convex and ovate, upper section light green and lower two-thirds brownish-red.

Flowers throughout the year.

Warm conditions.

P. chamberlainianum subsp. *liemiana* Fowl. 1971 (O.D.)

P. victoria-regina (Sander) M. W. Wood subsp. *liemianum* (Fowl.) M. W. Wood, *comb. nov.* 1976 (O.R.)

Subgenus *Otopedilum*. Section VII *Cochlopetalum* 2n = 32
Sumatra: Gunung Sinabung.

This subspecies has two basic forms, one with plain green leaves and the other distinctly tessellated. They are 15 to 22 cm (6 to 9 in) long, 4 to 6 cm (1½ to 2 ½ in) wide, and differ from the species and other subspecies by being ciliate around the entire margin. The plain leaf form is strongly marked on the underside with very fine red spots. The tessellated leaf form has only a few clusters of red spots at the extreme base of the leaf. These markings correlate with the colouring of the flowers: those plants which bear heavy red markings have deeper red markings on their flowers, richer purple spotting, and a wider white margin on the dorsal sepal.

The flower scape is dark brown, hirsute, up to 60 cm (24 in) tall, and bears up to 12 flowers.

The dorsal sepal is deep green with a wide, white margin, and bears faint brownish striations.

The petals are twisted, undulate, and widely spreading. Pale greenish-white with purple transverse (cross-banded) markings, stained with light-purple apically, and ciliate on both margins.

The lip is slightly more slender than in the other subspecies, pale pink, spotted with deeper pink. The in-folded side-lobes are creamish-white with brownish-red spots.

Ventral sepal is a smaller replica of the dorsal sepal.

The staminode is almost round, convex, purplish-green, and glossy.

Flowers in summer.

Warm conditions.

P. chamberlainianum forma *primulinum* var. *flavum* Fowl. 1973 (O.D.)

P. victoria-regina (Sander) M. W. Wood subsp. *primulinum* (M. W. Wood & P. Taylor) M. W. Wood, *comb. nov.* 1976 (O.R.)

Subgenus *Otopedilum*. Section VII. *Cochlopetalum* 2n = 32
Sumatra: Gunung Leuser.

Found growing at elevations of 400 to 500 metres (1300 to 1600 feet) in areas of high humidity and rainfall. It differs from the other members of the *Cochlopetalum* section by having narrower leaves, smaller flowers, and a differently shaped staminode.

Leaves are 10 to 30 cm (4 to 12 in) long, notched at the tips, velvety green, and a lighter shade on the undersides, which bear no purple markings (anthocyanins). The basal margins of the young leaves are ciliate and the upper surfaces are sometimes faintly tessellated.

The flower scape is up to 60 cm (24 in) tall and bears up to 20 flowers which open successively over a long period.

The dorsal sepal is almost circular and about 2.5 cm (1 in) wide. Medium green, with very faint, slightly darker green veins. The margin is ciliate and slightly paler in colour.

Petals are 8 cm (3 in) long and 2 cm ($\frac{3}{4}$ in) wide, pale, yellowish-green, twisted and undulate. They have very faint green longitudinal veins and ciliate margins.

The lip is 2.5 cm (1 in) long, bluntly rounded, and yellow in colour.

Ventral sepal is smaller than the dorsal, light green on front surface, and darker on back.

The staminode is dark green, lightening at apex and along upper margins. It is almost round, with a small upper incisure. The lower margin is flattened, and bears a small central, pendant uvula.

Flowers throughout the year.

Warm conditions.

P. chamberlainianum forma *primulinum* var. *flavescens* Fowl. 1973 (O.D.)

P. victoria-regina (Sander) M. W. Wood, subsp. *primulinum* (M. W. Wood & P. Taylor) forma *purpurescens* M. W. Wood, *forma nov.* 1976 (O.R.)

Subspecies *Otopedilum*. Section VII *Cochlopetalum* 2n = 32
Sumatra: Gunung Leuser.

Similar to the type form but differing in having purple markings on the undersides of the leaves, on the scape, bracts and petals.

The upper surface of the leaf varies from uniformly green to distinctly tessellated.

The lip is tinted pale purple, and the width beyond mid-length varies from parallel to expanded.

Flowers in summer.

Warm conditions.

P. charlesworthii (Rolfe) Stein 1893

Subgenus *Otopedilum*. Section IX *Neuropetalum* 2n = 26 (*Cyp. charlesworthii* Rolfe)
India, Bengal, Burma, Arrakan Mts.

Found growing on limestone mountains at an elevation of 1700 metres (5500 feet), always with a west or north-west aspect, and usually growing with *P. spicerianum*.

Leaves are dark green, up to 20 cm

(8 in) long and 2 cm ($\frac{3}{4}$ in) wide. Spotted on undersides with small purple dots.

The flower scape is up to 15 cm (6 in) tall, bearing a single flower about 6 cm ($2\frac{1}{2}$ in) wide. It is long lasting and of waxy texture.

Dorsal sepal is large and almost circular. Flat, rose-pink, with lines of darker pink radiating upwards from the base. Petals spreading horizontally, yellowish-brown with darker linear veins.

The lip is helmet-shaped and glossy, yellowish-brown with light purple veining. A narrow margin of light yellow adorns the rim of the aperture.

The ventral sepal is much smaller than the dorsal. Whitish-green with darker vertical veining, and slightly flushed with rose-pink on rear surfaces.

The staminode is white with a prominent glossy tubercle in its centre.

Flowers in autumn.
Cool conditions.

P. chiwuanum Tang & Wang 1940

Subgenus *Otopedilum*. Section XI *Cymato-petalum*
China: south-east Yunnan.

Found growing on rocks at an elevation of 700 metres (2200 feet),

this purple hued species is of erect habit, has thick hairy roots, and is closely related to *P. micranthum*.

The leaves are 20 to 40 cm (8 to 16 in) long and 1.6 to 2 cm ($\frac{5}{8}$ to $\frac{3}{4}$ in) wide, strap shaped, leathery, distinctly keeled, and with bi-dentate tips.

The flower scape is erect, single flowered, and clothed with thick, coarse, reddish-brown hairs.

The bract is ovate, smooth internally, and clothed externally with soft hairs.

The dorsal sepal is elliptically ovate with an obtuse apex clothed on back surface with sparse coarse hairs. It is 2.3 cm (1 in) long and 1.3 cm ($\frac{1}{2}$ in) wide, has ciliate margins and bears almost 15 vertical striations which extend for almost the full length.

The synsepalum is smooth on the front surface, hirsute on rear surface, and is 24 cm ($9\frac{1}{2}$ in) long and 1.7 cm ($\frac{5}{8}$ in) wide. The petals are 2.6 cm long and 9 mm ($\frac{3}{8}$ in) wide, narrow basally and gradually widening towards the tips, slightly twisted basally.

The labellum is about 1.9 cm ($\frac{3}{4}$ in) long and 9 mm ($\frac{3}{8}$ in) wide, with crescent shaped, infolded side lobes.

The staminode is sub-orbicular in shape, 7 mm ($\frac{1}{4}$ in) long and 5 mm ($\frac{3}{16}$ in) wide; front surface glabrous, and rear surface sparsely haired.

The ovary is clothed with dense

coarse hair, is 1.4 cm ($\frac{1}{2}$ in) long, and cylindrical-fusiform in shape.

Flowering season not known.
Intermediate conditions.

P. ciliolare (Rchb.f.) Pfitz. 1882

Subgenus *Otopedilum*. Section XV *Phacopetalum* (*Cyp. ciliolare* Rchb.f., *Cordula ciliolare* Rolfe)
Philippines: Dinagat, Mindanao.

This species usually bears only four leaves which are very similar to those of *P. argus*. They are light green with darker tessellation, up to 17 cm (7 in) long and 4 cm ($1\frac{1}{2}$ in) wide.

The flower scape is up to 30 cm (12 in) tall and bears a single flower about 7 cm (3 in) wide.

The dorsal sepal is broad basally, tapering sharply to a pointed apex. It is white with vertical green veins and brownish-purple basally with many small blackish-purple spots.

Petals are green basally, turning to white then becoming purple towards the tips. They bend down at about 45 degrees, are re-curved, and are ciliate on both margins. Closely spotted with blackish warts except at the tips. (In *P. superbiens* this spotting extends to the tips.)

The lip is purplish-brown, shaded with green basally. The in-folded side lobes are light greenish-yellow spotted with purple.

The ventral sepal is similar in shape to the dorsal but is smaller and is white with light green veining.

The staminode is cordate, whitish-green with darker green veining, and has a wide lower incisure which forms two lateral 'horns' and one central 'tooth', the latter projecting lower than the lateral 'horns'.

NOTE: A paper published by M. W. Wood and P. J. Cribb (*Curtis's Botanical Magazine*, 1981) describes this species as *P. superbiens* subsp. *ciliolare*. This paper also describes *P. superbiens* as *P. superbiens* subsp. *superbiens*, and indicates that *P. curtisii* is not a valid species.

P. concolor (Batem.) Stein 1865

Subgenus *Brachypetalum* 2n = 26 (*Cyp. concolor* Par. & Bat., *Cyp. tonkinense* Godefroy.)
South Thailand, south Burma, Cambodia, Laos, Vietnam.

Found growing in limestone crevices close to the coast at elevations of 300 to 1000 metres (about 1000 to 3300 feet).

Leaves are 7 to 15 cm ($2\frac{3}{4}$ to 6 in) long and 3 to 4 cm ($1\frac{1}{4}$ to $1\frac{1}{2}$ in) wide, slightly serrated at the tips. Dark green mottled with greyish-green, and spotted with reddish-purple on undersides.

The flower scape is short, only 5 to 8 cm (2 to 3 in) long, bearing one to three flowers up to 7 cm ($2\frac{3}{4}$ in) wide.

Dorsal sepal is almost circular and variable in colour. Cream to pale yellow, lightly spotted with purple, and tinged with light green. Apex-hooded.

The petals are oval and concave, slightly drooping, and the same colour and markings as the dorsal sepal.

The lip is narrowly egg-shaped, with in-folded side lobes which almost meet. Same colour as the other segments, but with finer and more sparse spotting.

Ventral sepal is slightly shorter than the dorsal, much narrower, and spotted only on the basal half.

The staminode is cordate and glossy, very pale yellow, with finer spotting of the same colour as the other segments.

Flowers in summer and autumn.
Intermediate conditions.

P. curtisii (Rchb.f.) Stein 1883

Subgenus *Otopedilum*. Section XV *Phacopetalum*. 2n = 36 (*Cyp. curtisii* Rchb.f.) Sumatra: Padang.

Leaves few, elliptical, 20 cm (8 in) long and 6 cm ($2\frac{1}{2}$ in) wide. Light green, upper surfaces tessellated with darker green.

Flower scape up to 30 cm (12 in) tall, deep purple, hirsute, and bearing a single flower about 9 cm ($3\frac{1}{2}$ in) wide.

The dorsal sepal is broad, short, and acutely pointed. It is bright green with a white apex and margin. The many vertical veins are purple, turning green towards the apex. Some of the veins are green for their full length. The whole segment is slightly concave and not reflexed basally as in *P. superbiens*.

Petals are twisted and pendulous, greenish-pink basally, turning to a pale pink apically. Both margins are spotted and ciliate. Basal sections are darker and marked with closely spaced, purplish-brown, longitudinal lines and spots.

The lip is very large, dark greenish-maroon, with darker purple veining. The rear surface is shaded with lighter green. The in-folded side lobes are light rose-pink with deeper rose spotting.

Ventral sepal is whitish-green with darker green veining and is much smaller than the dorsal.

The staminode is whitish-green with darker green markings. The shape of its lower incisure forms two prominent 'horns' on the extremities of the lower margin.

Flowers in autumn.
Warm conditions.

P. dayanum (Rchb.f.) Stein 1862

Subgenus *Otopedilum*. Section XIV *Blepharopetalum* 2n = 36 (*Cyp. dayanum* Rchb.f.)
North-east Borneo: Mt Kinabalu.

Found growing at elevations of 300 to 1500 metres (1000 to 5000 feet).

Leaves about 18 cm (7 in) long and 4 cm ($1\frac{1}{2}$ in) wide. Pale yellowish-green, mottled with darker green, and having a serrated tip. The undersides are lighter in colour.

The flower scape is about 25 cm (10 in) tall and bears a single flower about 15 cm (6 in) wide.

The dorsal sepal is ovate and elongated, with the upper margin pinched together forming a hood, the whole segment leaning forward. It is white, evenly veined with green, 5 to 6 cm (2 to $2\frac{1}{2}$ in) tall, and 3 cm ($1\frac{1}{4}$ in) wide.

Petals are about 7 cm (3 in) long, narrow, slightly pendulous, and fringed on both margins with long black hairs. They are brownish-green basally, shading to rose-purple towards the tips.

The lip is brownish-purple veined with green, rather acutely pointed at the 'toe', and having a narrow margin of yellowish-green around the aperture. The in-folded side-lobes are densely spotted with small purplish warts.

Ventral sepal is smaller than the dorsal but similar in colouring.

The disc is cordate (heart-shaped), light green with darker green markings centrally, and is ciliate. The lower incisure is reported to vary within the species, thus forming either one or three distinct 'teeth'.

Flowers in summer.
Warm conditions.

NOTE: Just prior to going to press, J. A. Fowlie, MD, kindly advised me that plants of *P. petri* and *P. burbidgei*, which he personally collected on Mt Kinabalu (Borneo), have flowered and proved to be merely a high elevation race of *P. dayanum* of two completely differently patterned leaf ecotypes. They are therefore now reduced to synonyms of *P. dayanum* (high elevation race).

P. delenatii Guillaumin 1926

Subgenus *Brachypetalum* 2n = 26 (*Cyp. delenatii* Guillaumin)
North and central Vietnam.

This very beautiful species is unusual in that it is faintly fragrant during the daylight hours. It is found growing at low elevations in the crevices of limestone mountains.

Leaves are very thick and rigid, dark green with light green tessellation on upper surfaces. The lower surfaces are light green with reddish-purple mottling.

The flower scape is up to 20 cm

(8 in) tall and bears one or two flowers.

The dorsal sepal is oval, 'pinched', and pointed at the apex. It is white in colour, flushed with rose-pink, and has a velvety texture.

Petals are rounded, white, flushed with light pink.

The lip is almost spherical, white and rose-pink, lightly stained with lavender.

Ventral sepal is a smaller replica of the dorsal sepal.

The staminode is rhomboid in shape, convex, and deep pink except for two prominent markings, one at the lower extremity, and the other just above the centre.

Flowers in spring or early summer. Warm conditions.

P. dianthum Tang & Wang 1939

Subgenus *Otopedilum*. Section V *Mystropetalum*
China: Yunnan, Kwangsi; North Vietnam (adjacent to Chinese border).

This beautiful species closely resembles *P. parishii* but differs in having a glabrous (devoid of hair) ovary, and a slightly differently shaped pouch.

An erect plant of terrestrial habit, about 30 cm (12 in) high, and having a very short rhizome with thick and hairy roots.

The leaves are strap-like, blunted, smooth, upright, and spreading. Apex unequally bidentate, 20 to 23 cm (8 to 9 in) long, and 3.5 cm ($1\frac{3}{8}$ in) wide.

Flower scape is upright but slightly bent, two flowered, up to 30 cm (12 in) tall, and moderately papillose.

Bracts are subovate, cucullate, with rounded, tridentate apex. Outer surface sparsely papillose.

The showy flower is about 10 cm (4 in) wide, purplish, and whitish-green. The dorsal sepal is about 4.5 cm ($1\frac{3}{4}$ in) long and 1.8 cm (about $\frac{3}{4}$ in) wide, oblong elliptical, with an acute apex, bearing about 19 veins, the middle vein being distinctly keeled.

Petals are two to three times longer than the sepals, widely spreading but pendulous, twisted and undulate. Wide basally, gradually narrowing towards tips. Linear, attenuate, accuminate and thin at apex. Somewhat hirsute on both surfaces, margins ciliate, and bearing scattered warts, 9.5 cm ($3\frac{3}{4}$ in) long, and 8 mm ($\frac{5}{16}$ in) wide.

Synsepalum smooth on front surface and hirsute at rear. Narrowly oblong, 3.5 cm ($1\frac{3}{8}$ in) long, and 1.8 cm (about $\frac{3}{4}$ in) wide.

The pouch is 4.5 cm ($1\frac{3}{4}$ in) long, smooth outside and hirsute internally. Column short, robust, with under surface hirsute.

The staminode is distinctly obovate with a blunt apex. Hirsute basally, but otherwise smooth except for finely ciliate margin. 14 cm ($5\frac{1}{2}$ in) long, and 9 mm ($\frac{3}{8}$ in) wide.

The ovary is cylindrical, fusiform, and distinctly glabrous.

Intermediate conditions.

P. druryi (Beddome) Stein 1868

Subgenus *Otopedilum*. Section X *Thiopetalum* 2n = 30 (*Cyp. druryi* Beddome) Southern India: Travancore Hills.

This species has the unusual habit of growing from a long and stout creeping rhizome and is found growing in the gorges of the Cardamon Mountains at elevations of 1500 to 2000 metres (5000 to 6600 feet).

The leaves are up to 25 cm (10 in) long, are stout, rigid, and apple-green in colour.

Flower scape is up to 25 cm (10 in) tall, thick, erect, and bears a single flower.

The dorsal sepal is broad and curves forward, greenish-yellow, with a very conspicuous and broad blackish-brown vertical stripe. The margins and back surfaces are ciliate.

Petals are broad, curved forward, and ciliate. They are golden-yellow with broad, blackish, median lines, and bear scattered black warts on their basal sections.

The lip is large, helmet-shaped, pale yellow and spotted on the inside with reddish-purple.

Ventral sepal is slightly larger than the dorsal but much paler in colour and bears two narrow blackish-brown vertical stripes.

The staminode is light yellow with a deeper hued mark in its centre. Broadly ovate with a wide, V-shaped upper incisure. The centre of the lower margin bears a small pendant uvula.

Flowers in spring.

Warm conditions.

P. esquirolei Schltr. 1919

Subgenus *Otopedilum*. Section VIII *Stictopetalum* 2n = 26 South China, North Thailand.

Leaves are 24 cm ($9\frac{1}{2}$ in) long and 2.5 cm (1 in) wide, notched apically, and distinctly keeled. Dark green, glossy, and very faintly marbled on upper surfaces. The undersides are lighter green, dull, and unmarbled.

The flower scape is about 20 cm (8 in) tall, green basally, becoming purplish-green towards the flower.

The dorsal sepal is about 4 cm ($1\frac{1}{2}$ in) wide, broadly ovate, tapering towards the apex. Greenish, with purple-brown suffusions and bearing about 14 darker purple vertical veins.

Petals are about 7 cm ($2\frac{3}{4}$ in) long and 3 cm ($1\frac{1}{4}$ in) wide at the tips, narrowing to 2 cm ($\frac{3}{4}$ in) basally, and prominently undulate for the basal

4 cm ($1\frac{1}{2}$ in) of the upper margin. The broadly rounded apical section is a striking rose-purple shade, which changes to a light creamish-green basally. This section bears purple spots which become closer together, lighten in colour, and finally merge into the apical section.

The lip is 2 cm ($\frac{3}{4}$ in) wide and 3 cm ($1\frac{1}{4}$ in) long, helmet-shaped, and having in-folded side-lobes which almost meet. It is creamish-green, spotted with rose-purple.

The ventral sepal is basally the same width as the dorsal, tapering to a rounded tip. It is 3.5 cm ($1\frac{1}{2}$ in) long, light creamish-green, with purplish-brown veins.

The staminode is 1 cm ($\frac{1}{2}$ in) wide and 1.5 cm ($\frac{5}{8}$ in) deep, creamish-green basally and around the margins. In the centre is a prominent, light-green glistening tubercle. The lower section is deep purple. In the upper section are two prominent white 'eyes' which are surrounded by tiny spots of deep purple.

Flowers in spring.

Intermediate conditions.

NOTE: Although very similar to *P. hirsutissimum*, this species is much more sparsely haired on all its segments.

P. exul (O'Brien) Stein 1892

Subgenus *Otopedilum*. Section IX *Neuropetalum* 2n = 26 (*Cyp. exul* O'Brien)
Thailand: Krabi Gulf, west of Isthmus of Kra.

Found growing at low elevations in humus filled rock crevices.

Leaves are up to 20 cm (8 in) long and 2 cm ($\frac{3}{4}$ in) wide, similar to *P. insigne* and sometimes very faintly mottled.

The flower scape is about 12 cm ($4\frac{3}{4}$ in) tall and bears a single flower which resembles a small form of *P. insigne*.

The dorsal sepal is broad, greenish-yellow with wide, white margins and heavily spotted with blackish-brown. The apex is slightly 'pinched' and bent forward.

Petals are yellowish-brown with faint purple veining, finely spotted with blackish-brown basally, and have a darker brown horizontal mid-line.

The lip is large, yellow basally, shading upwards to greenish-brown.

Ventral sepal is much larger than the dorsal, apple-green with a narrow white ciliate margin, and a few small, blackish spots.

Flowers in autumn.

Cool conditions.

P. fairieanum (Ldl.) Stein 1857 (re-discovered 1905)

Subgenus *Otopedilum*. Section XII. *Cerato-petalum* 2n = 26 (*Cyp. fairieanum* Ldl.) Himalayas, Assam, northern Burma.

Found growing at elevations of 1200 to 3000 metres (4000 to 9900 feet) on the edges of forests alongside high river banks. Those growing at high elevations are subject to frosts. For almost 50 years this species was thought to be extinct but was re-discovered in the Khasi Hills district of India. A larger form was also discovered in the ranges of Northern Burma.

Leaves are dull green, channelled, 15 cm (6 in) long and 2 cm (3 in) wide, and have a slight serration at the tip.

The flower scape is slender, pur-plish, pubescent, and up to 25 cm (10 in) tall. The single flower is 6 cm ($2\frac{1}{2}$ in) wide and very variable in colour.

The dorsal sepal is large and distinctive, broadly elliptical, with pronounced undulate margins. White in colour, it is streaked and nettled with violet-purple.

Petals are whitish, with purple and green striations, the margins are studded with tufts of black hairs, and have very pronounced undulations. The shape of the petals resembles the horns of a buffalo.

The lip is greenish-purple with darker purple veins and has creamish-white, in-folded side-lobes.

Ventral sepal is smaller than the dorsal but similar in colour.

The staminode is cordate, light green, with darker green and purple markings.

Flowers in late autumn.

Cool conditions.

P. fowliei Birk 1981

Subgenus *Otopedilum*. Section XV *Phaco-petalum* Philippines: Brook's Point, Palawan Is.

Found growing as a lithophyte on limestone in pockets of leaf mould at an elevation of 700 metres (about 2300 feet), this new species is closely related to *P. hennisianum* and *P. lawrenceanum*.

Leaves are 10 to 14 cm (4 to $5\frac{1}{2}$ in) long and 2 to 3 cm ($\frac{3}{4}$ to $1\frac{1}{4}$ in) wide, narrowly elliptical, coloured a distinctive bluish-grey-green, and tessellated with darker tones.

The flower scape is 20 to 28 cm (8 to 11 in) tall, and clothed with short hairs.

The dorsal sepal is white, striped with reddish-purple, and reflexed at the apex. It is broadly elliptic, 4 to 6 cm ($1\frac{1}{2}$ to $2\frac{1}{2}$ in) high and 3 to 4 cm ($1\frac{1}{4}$ to $1\frac{1}{2}$ in) wide.

Petals are 4 to 6 cm ($1\frac{1}{2}$ to $2\frac{1}{2}$ in) long, 1.5 cm ($\frac{5}{8}$ in) wide, emerging at right angles then becoming distinctly pendulous. Greenish basally, with darker green longitudinal lines, and suffused apically with light purple. The upper margins bear up to 15 prominent hairy warts, while the lower margins are more sparsely furnished with smaller warts. The mid-line is marked with a series of longitudinal lines.

The lip is brownish-yellow, veined with darker brown. About 4 cm ($1\frac{1}{2}$ in) long and 3 cm ($1\frac{1}{4}$ in) wide, slightly swollen below mid-length.

Ventral sepal is 3 cm ($1\frac{1}{4}$ in) long and 2 cm ($\frac{3}{4}$ in) wide, similar in colouring to the dorsal sepal.

The staminode is most distinctive in its very deep lower central incisure which forms two long, projecting 'horns'. Between these 'horns' is a pendant uvula.

Flowers in summer.

Warm conditions.

P. gardineri (Guillem.) Stein 1887

Subgenus *Anotopedilum*. Section III *Coryopedilum*
Indonesia: Jobi Is.

Re-discovered in 1979, this rare species appears to be similar in plant habit to that of *P. praestans*. Its leaves are about 19 cm ($7\frac{1}{2}$ in) long and 3.5 cm ($1\frac{1}{2}$ in) wide.

The flower scape is clothed with fine brown hairs, and usually bears two flowers which are darker in colour than those of *P. praestans*.

Dorsal sepal about 4 cm ($1\frac{1}{2}$ in) long and 2.5 cm (1 in) wide.

The pouch is veined with brown, and projects horizontally.

The staminode is reddish, rather square in shape, and bears prominent hairy warts on its side and upper margins. The lower margin has a deep central incisure with a light yellow uvula.

Warm conditions.

P. glanduliferum (Blume) Stein 1848 (O.D.)

Subgenus *Anotopedilum*. Section III *Coryopedilum*
North-west New Guinea.

This species does not appear to be currently under cultivation and in some quarters is considered to be synonymous with *P. praestans*. However, research recently carried out by James Asher, and comparison of the original chromolith of *P. glanduliferum* with photographs of *P. praestans* indicate that they are indeed separate species.

The following condensed descrip-

P. esquirolei

P. fairieanum

P. fowliei

P. glaucophyllum

P. godefroyae

P. gardineri

P. gratrixianum

P. hookerae

Top: *P. haynaldianum*
Centre: *P. hennisianum*
Bottom: *P. hirsutissimum*

P. insigne

P. insigne var. *albomarginatum*

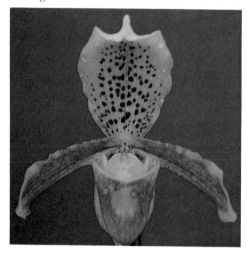

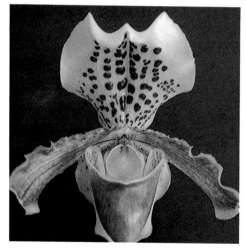

P. insigne var. *Harefield Hall*

P. insigne var. *Sanderae*

P. johorensis

P. kolopakingii

P. javanicum

P. lawrenceanum

P. linii

P. laevigatum

P. leucochilum

P. micranthum

P. lowii

P. mastersianum

P. moquetteanum

P. nigritum

P. niveum

P. parishii

tion is translated from the original Latin description in Blume's *Rumphia*, 1848, 4:56 t, 198:

Leaves leathery, rigid, linear with blunted or rounded tips, grooved basally. Usually four to seven, 14 to 16 cm [$5\frac{1}{2}$ to $6\frac{1}{2}$ in] long, 2 to 3 cm [$\frac{3}{4}$ to $1\frac{1}{4}$ in] wide, erect, dark green and untessellated. Flower scape hairy, dingy purple, two-flowered with a large single bract.

Dorsal sepal oblong, lanceolate, acuminate, often with the margins rolled back. Light rose, shading to pale green.

Petals linear, very acuminate, undulating at the margins, bearing bearded glands at the base. Light rose shading to pale green centrally.

Labellum large, inflated, slipper-shaped, margins at the base on both sides rolled inward and upward, producing a sharply pointed appendage. Yellow, fading to light brown, veins above the median line dark violet, strongly branching.

Staminode arched upwards with a depression from above, hairy, elongated in front into a keeled, glabrous beak.

Synsepalum emarginate, longer than the dorsal sepal.

Warm conditions.

P. glaucophyllum J.J.Sm. 1900 (O.D.)

P. victoria-regina (Sander) M. W. Wood subsp. *glaucophyllum* (J.J.Sm.) M. W. Wood, *comb. nov.* 1976 (O.R.)
Subgenus *Otopedilum*. Section VII *Cochlopetalum* 2n = 36, 37
East Java: near Turon.

Found growing in small amounts of humus in rock pockets on the slopes of volcanic mountains at elevations of 200 to 300 metres (about 660 to 1000 feet).

Leaves are 25 cm (10 in) long and 5 cm (2 in) wide, obtuse, keeled, and of a distinctive bluish-green (glaucous) colour. The undersides are spotted with purple.

The flower scape is up to 40 cm (16 in) tall, bearing many flowers which open successively over a long period. Each flower emerges from a short, hairy bract.

The dorsal sepal is almost circular, light brownish-green with a white margin, and having about 12 dark brownish-red striations in the form of closely spaced spots.

Petals are spread horizontally, twisted, undulate, and ciliate on both margins. White in colour with scattered dark-purple lines and spots.

The lip is large, whitish-green blushed with rosy-pink, and lightly spotted with crimson. The margin is white, and the in-folded side-lobes spotted with brown.

Ventral sepal is pale green and smaller than the dorsal.

The staminode is rhombic in shape and distinctly depressed in its centre. The upper section is light creamish-green turning to deep purplish-brown basally.

Flowers in summer.

Warm conditions.

P. godefroyae (Godefroy) Stein 1883

Subgenus *Brachypetalum* 2n = 26 (*Cyp. godefroyae* G.)
Thailand: Birdsnest Is., east of Isthmus of Kra.

A small growing plant with foliage similar to *P. bellatulum*. It grows on limestone cliffs at an altitude of only 35 metres (about 114 feet), where it receives almost full sunlight.

Leaves are 8 to 12 cm (3 to 5 in) long and 3 to 4 cm (1 to $1\frac{1}{2}$ in) wide, distinctly keeled and notched at the apex. Under surfaces are dull, dark green, and mottled with greyish-green. The undersides are dark purple with no green colouration whatsoever.

The flower scape is 3 to 8 cm (1 to 3 in) long, pubescent, pale green with purple spotting.

The dorsal sepal is distinctly keeled and hooded, rounded, with a notch at the apex. Dull white to creamy yellow, densely spotted with deep brownish-purple. The lower margins are slightly undulate.

Petals are almost circular, slightly cupped, same colour and markings as the dorsal sepal.

The lip is cream and unspotted except at the sides close to the point of attachment. The in-folded side-lobes meet, and are closely spotted with tiny, deep-purple markings.

Ventral sepal is smaller than the dorsal but of the same colour. It is cupped and very sparsely spotted with brownish-purple on the front surface. The rear surface is much more densely spotted.

The staminode is small and squarish in shape with a distinct 'tooth' projecting downwards from the centre of the lower margin. It is the same colour as the other segments, covered with tiny purple spots, and having a bright yellow depression in its centre.

Flowers in spring and summer.
Intermediate conditions.

P. gratrixianum (Sander) Guillaum. 1905

Subgenus *Otopedilum*. Section IX *Neuropetalum* 2n = 26
Central Vietnam: Annam.

Leaves dark green, 15 to 22 cm (6 to 9 in) long, and untessellated.

The flower scape is dark green, hirsute and bearing a single flower.

Dorsal sepal is large and rounded, narrowing and re-curving basally, with a slightly hooded and in-folded apex. It is white with a yellowish-brown centre, and bears about 30 brownish-black spots distributed from the base almost to the apex in a narrow mid-line area.

The petals are brownish-yellow,

very glossy, slightly undulate on upper margins, bearing darker brown longitudinal veins. The colour is lighter below the prominent mid-line.

The lip is similar in colour to the petals and has very prominent auricles.

The ventral sepal is much smaller than the dorsal and is greenish-yellow.

The staminode is inverted cordate in shape, verrucose, golden-brown, and bears a prominent and glossy tubercle.

The flower resembles both *P. insigne* and *P. exul*, and is about the same size as the former.

Warm conditions.

Flowers in winter.

P. haynaldianum (Rchb.f.) Stein 1874

Subgenus *Otopedilum*. Section VI *Pardalo-petalum* 2n = 26 (*Cyp. haynaldianum* Rchb.f.)
Philippines: Luzon.

Found growing on mountainsides at elevations of over 1000 metres (about 3300 feet).

Leaves up to 30 cm (12 in) long and 4 cm ($1\frac{1}{2}$ in) wide, medium green, leathery texture, untessellated, and with notched tips.

Flower scape up to 50 cm (20 in) tall, green, pubescent, and bearing up to six flowers which are distinctive in their narrow and spreading segments.

The dorsal sepal is narrowly oval with slight apical undulations, pale green with a yellowish tinge, blotched basally with brown, and pinkish towards the apex. About eight lighter brown striations extend upwards from the base but fade out slightly past mid-height.

Petals are about 6 cm ($2\frac{1}{2}$ in) long, narrow, pointed, and drooping slightly, widening towards the tips. The basal half is greenish-yellow with large brown spots, while the apical half is twisted, unspotted, and brownish-yellow in colour.

The lip is helmet-shaped, greenish-yellow suffused with purple, and has glossy white in-folded side-lobes.

Ventral sepal is smaller than the dorsal, white with green veins.

The staminode is 11 mm ($\frac{1}{2}$ in) long and 9 mm ($\frac{1}{4}$ in) wide, light creamish-green, darkening towards the centre. Inverted heart-shaped with a central basal cleft curving upwards at the rear to form a spur. A prominent greenish tubercle is borne on the front surface just above the cleft.

Flowers in summer.

Intermediate conditions.

P. hennisianum (Wood) Fowl. 1977

Subgenus *Otopedilum*. Section XV *Phacopetalum*
Philippines: Visayan area.

Leaves are 14 cm ($5\frac{1}{2}$ in) long and 3 cm ($1\frac{1}{4}$ in) wide, keeled, and notched at the tips. Mid-green with very faint darker green marbling.

The flower scape is 22 cm ($8\frac{3}{4}$ in) tall, purple, pubescent, and bearing a single flower.

The dorsal sepal is white, with prominent bright-green vertical stripes. The two stripes adjacent to the margins are purplish-red. The margins are slightly in-curved basally.

Petals are white, with bright green horizontal veins which change to purple apically. The extremities are clear white and both margins bear closely spaced blackish warts. In some forms these warts appear near the mid-line also.

The lip is rich purple-brown with veining of brownish-black. The in-folded side-lobes meet and are light green with many small purplish warts.

Ventral sepal is light green with darker green stripes. It is about half the size of the dorsal sepal.

The staminode is light green with darker green markings, and has a narrow upper incisure. The lower incisure is wide, and forms two prominent 'horns' on the extremities of the lower margin. A small black 'tooth' projects downwards from the centre of the lower incisure.

Flowers in summer.

Warm conditions.

P. hirsutissimum (Ldl. ex Hook.) Stein 1857

Subgenus *Otopedilum*. Section VIII *Stictopetalum* 2n = 26 (*Cyp. hirsutissimum* Ldl.)
Himalayas, Assam, Khasia Hills.

Found growing at elevations of 1000 to 1300 metres (about 3300 to 4300 feet), usually as a terrestrial but often as an epiphyte or a lithophyte.

Leaves are up to 30 cm (12 in) long, keeled, deep green, untessellated, and resembling *P. insigne*.

The flower scape is up to 30 cm (12 in) tall, green, hirsute, and bearing a single flower up to 11 cm ($4\frac{1}{2}$ in) wide.

Dorsal sepal is large and cordate, keeled, and with a vivid green margin. The basal and central areas are also green, but are densely spotted with blackish-purple. The entire back surface is thickly haired.

The petals are large, spreading horizontally and slightly twisted apically. They are prominently undulate on the basal half, particularly on the upper margin. Basally they are dark green spotted with purple, clothed with blackish hairs.

The apical section is wider and entirely rose-purple in colour.

The lip is large, dull green tinged with purple, and densely spotted with small blackish warts.

Ventral sepal is smaller than the dorsal, ovate, pale green with purple veining, and densely hirsute on back surface.

The staminode is light green, finely spotted with purple. The lower central section bears a large green mark, above which are two prominent white spots.

Flowers in autumn or early summer.

Cool conditions.

P. hookerae (Rchb.f.) Stein 1864

Subgenus *Otopedilum*. Section *Hookerae* Fowl. 2n = 28 (*Cyp. hookerae* Rchb.f., *Cyp. barbatum* Ldl. var. *hookerae* Regel.) North Borneo: Sabah, Sarawak.

Found growing in dense shade at elevations of 900 to 1100 metres (about 3000 to 3600 feet), sometimes with *P. stonei*.

Leaves are up to 14 cm ($5\frac{1}{2}$ in) long, blunted, dark green, mottled with creamy-yellow.

The flower scape is tall, hirsute, and single-flowered.

The dorsal sepal is hooded and acutely pointed at the tip. Creamy-white with a central overlay of greenish-yellow, and with veins of dark green extending from the base to the edge of the lighter coloured margin.

Petals are ciliate, spatulate, and pointed apically, rosy-lavender except for the basal sections which are tinged with yellow and finely spotted with blackish-purple.

The lip is expanded beyond mid-length, is yellowish basally, and deepens to a brownish-yellow at the rim.

Ventral sepal is ovate, pale yellow, and smaller than the dorsal.

The staminode is rounded, concave, rosy-purple with a yellow centre and upper margin. The centre of the lower margin bears a narrow central cleft.

Flowers in spring or early summer.

Warm conditions.

P. insigne (Wall. ex Ldl.) Stein 1821

Subgenus *Otopedilum*. Section IX *Neuropetalum* 2n = 26, 39 (*Cyp. insigne* Wall.) Himalayas, Sylhet, Nepal, Assam.

This species, probably the best known and most widely cultivated of the genus, is found growing at an elevation of 2000 metres (about 6600 feet) in positions fully exposed to the southerly monsoonal rains. It thrives in cold conditions, is a prolific flowerer, and is an ideal subject for the novice orchid grower as its cultivation presents so few problems.

Leaves are bright green, narrow, and 20 to 30 cm (8 to 12 in) long.

The flower scape is up to 28 cm (11 in) tall, green, covered with dense purplish down, and bearing a single flower up to 12 cm (5 in) wide.

The dorsal sepal is large, ovate, with the apex bent forward and lower margins slightly folded back. Light apple-green, with many small purplish spots. The apical 2 cm ($\frac{3}{4}$ in) section is pure white.

Petals are broad, slightly undulate and drooping. Yellowish to pale green, slightly tinged with brown, and bearing purplish-brown longitudinal lines,

The lip is yellowish-green, flushed and veined with brown, and having a narrow margin of lighter green.

Ventral sepal is light green and about the same length as the dorsal. It narrows to an acute in-folded tip and bears several vertical rows of purple dots.

The staminode is clear yellow with a glistening, darker yellow tubercle in its centre.

Flowers in winter.

Cold conditions.

P. insigne var. Harefield Hall

All segments of the flower much larger than in the type form.

Scape up to 30 cm (12 in) tall, dark, purplish-brown, and densely haired.

Dorsal sepal up to 8 cm (3 in) wide, rounded, with a wide, white, margin. Centre section is light green and bears about 70 large reddish-brown spots which diminish in size towards the base.

Petals are up to 7 cm ($2\frac{3}{4}$ in) long. Undulate, light green, with reddish-brown horizontal lines. The basal parts of the lower margins bear reddish spots.

The lip is cordate and up to 5 cm (2 in) long. The rear and side surfaces are light green, and the front is flushed with light reddish-brown. The margin of the aperture is light green.

Ventral sepal is the same size as the dorsal but narrower, and sparsely spotted with reddish brown.

P. insigne var. Sanderae

Flower scape green and up to 25 cm (10 in) tall.

Dorsal sepal very light green with wide, white margins which are undulate. The lower section bears sparse and very faint fine, brownish spotting.

Petals are up to 6 cm ($2\frac{1}{2}$ in) long, slightly drooping, and with undulate margins. Very light green, lightening towards the tips, and bearing faint horizontal stripes of slightly darker green.

The lip is helmet-shaped, 3 cm ($1\frac{1}{4}$ in) wide, and 4 cm ($1\frac{1}{2}$ in) long, and very light yellowish-green.

Ventral sepal is the same length as the dorsal but slightly narrower. Very light yellowish-green with faint green striations.

The staminode is rounded, bright yellow, with a prominent yellowish-orange tubercle in its centre.

P. insigne var. albomarginatum

Almost identical to var. *Sanderae* except for complete absence of spotting on the dorsal sepal and being slightly larger in all segments.

P. javanicum (Reinw.) Stein 1823

Subgenus *Otopedilum*. Section XIV *Blepharopetalum* 2n = 38 (*Cyp. javanicum* Reinw.)
Indonesia: Java, Bali.

Found growing in dense shade at elevations of 1000 to 1500 metres (about 3300 to 5000 feet).

Leaves are 10 to 15 cm (4 to 6 in) long and 3 to 4 cm (1 to $1\frac{1}{2}$ in) wide. Pointed, greyish-green, with small and widely spaced tessellations of darker green.

The flower scape is up to 30 cm (12 in) tall, reddish-purple, and bears a single flower.

The dorsal sepal is short, broad, and acutely pointed. Pale green, mottled with greenish-purple, and bearing about 15 dark green vertical striations. The margin is whitish-pink.

Petals are pale green, tipped with rose-purple, ciliate on both margins, and densely dotted with blackish warts except for the tips.

The lip is brownish-green, pale green veined with purple on lower surfaces. The in-folded side-lobes, which almost meet, are pale green speckled with purple.

Ventral sepal is the same length as the dorsal but narrower.

The staminode is light green with darker markings in its centre and bears a small white mark just below the upper margin. The lower margin has two large incisures which form three downward pointing lobes.

Flowers in autumn.

Warm conditions.

P. johorensis Fowl. & Yap. 1972

Subgenus *Otopedilum*. Section XIII *Spathopetalum*
Southern Malaya: Gunong Panti.

Found growing in leaf mould in shaded positions at elevations of 500 to 750 metres (about 1600 to 2300 feet).

Leaves 20 cm (8 in) long and 3 cm ($1\frac{1}{4}$ in) wide with a prominent mid-vein running full length, and having tridentate tips. Dark bluish-green, very faintly tessellated on upper surfaces and plain, lighter green beneath.

The flower scape is up to 45 cm (18 in) tall, clothed with dense brown hairs, and bearing a single flower about 8 cm (3 in) wide.

The dorsal sepal is ovate, acutely pointed, pubescent on back surface, and with upper side margins rolled forward. Pale green, with darker green vertical veining. Lower side margins reflexed basally and tip curved forward forming a hood.

Petals are narrow, widening towards the tips. Green basally, changing abruptly to rose-pink at mid-length. The upper margins are undulate basally and bear blackish spots.

The lip is whitish basally, suffused with brownish-yellow above, and has a narrow light-yellow margin around the aperture. Sparse pink veining covers the entire segment, and the interior surface is light pink with prominent dark-pink spotting. The auricles are large and conspicuous, accentuating the deep, central cleft in the aperture rim.

Ventral sepal is smaller than the dorsal, apple-green, and pubescent on back surface. The basal section is slightly reflexed.

The staminode is horizontally oval with its upper incisure narrow and rounded, and its lower incisure much wider and more pointed at its extremities.

Flowers in autumn.
Warm conditions.

P. kolopakingii Fowl. 1983

Subgenus *Anotopedilum* Section IV *Prenipedilum*
Indonesia: headwaters of Barito River, central Kalimantan.

This new species, the largest member of the genus, is found growing on rocky cliffs over steep gorges at an elevation of 650 metres (2000 feet).

It is semi-terrestrial to lithophytic in habit and has abbreviated rhizomes which produce close clumps of leaves.

The roots are fleshy, 24 cm ($9\frac{1}{2}$ in) long and 5 to 8 mm ($\frac{5}{16}$ in) wide. The leaves are eight to 12 in number and reach 60 cm (24 in) in length and 8 cm (3 in) in width; strap-shaped and plain dark green with an occasional hint of faint marbling.

The flower scape reaches 70 cm (28 in) in height and 8 mm ($\frac{5}{16}$ in) in diameter and bears six to 14 flowers which all open at the same time.

The dorsal sepal is whitish, narrowly elliptical, 5 to 6.5 cm (2 in) long, 2.5 to 3.5 cm (1 in) wide and bears nine to 15 longitudinal stripes, seven to nine of which extend full height, and five to seven of which end halfway up the segment.

The synsepalum is of similar shape and colour but is slightly smaller. It bears fewer longitudinal stripes, on a creamy-whitish ground colour.

The petals are strap-shaped, spreading at about 45 degrees, 5 to 7 cm (2 to 3 in) long and 6 to 8 mm ($\frac{5}{16}$ in) wide basally, tapering immediately to form very narrow triangular shapes with a slight twist towards the tips. Green in colour, with seven to nine longitudinal stripes of a faint reddish colour.

The lip is of inverted helmet shape and bears a 1.5 to 2.5 cm ($\frac{3}{4}$ to 1 in) claw, is 4 to 5.6 cm ($1\frac{1}{2}$ to 2 in) long and 2 to 2.8 cm ($\frac{3}{4}$ to 1 in) wide. It is greenish towards the toe with brownish veining which creates the illusion that the segment is brownish in colour. The base of the toe is pure white where the veining fades out.

The staminode is vertically ovate, 1 to 1.5 cm ($\frac{1}{2}$ to $\frac{3}{4}$ in) long and 8 to 10 mm ($\frac{5}{16}$ in) wide. Upper and side margins bear copious amounts of twisted hairs similar to those in *P. stonei*. The apex is truncated and has a beak-like protruberance not evident in *P. stonei*.

This species is easily distinguished from *P. rothschildianum* by the latter's famous staminode which appears like a 'knee' with a 90 degree bend in it.

Flowers in summer.
Warm conditions.

P. laevigatum (Batem.) Stein 1865 (O.D.)

Subgenus *Anotopedilum*. Section III *Coryopedilum* 2n = 26
Philippines.

Very similar to, and sharing an intermediate species relationship with *P. philippinense*, this species owes its name to its lack of hair (*laevigatum* meaning 'smooth' or 'slippery'.) Its petals are pendant and untwisted, not outstretched as in *P. philippinense*.

Flowers in summer.
Warm conditions.

P. lawrenceanum (Rchb.f.) Stein 1878

Subgenus *Otopedilum*. Section XV *Phaco-petalum* 2n = 36, 40 (*Cyp. lawrenceanum* Rchb.f.)
North Borneo.

Found growing along river banks at elevations of 300 to 500 metres (about 1000 to 1600 feet).

Leaves are 20 to 25 cm (8 to 10 in) long, dark green, beautifully tessellated with yellowish-green.

The flower scape is up to 40 cm (16 in) tall, purplish, hirsute, and bears a single flower up to 12 cm (5 in) wide.

The dorsal sepal is rounded, white, with broad vertical veins of brownish-purple which become green basally.

The petals are widely spread, up to 6 cm ($2\frac{1}{2}$ in) long and 1.5 cm ($\frac{1}{2}$ in) wide. Green with purplish tips, and reddish basally. The margins are ciliate with a few blackish warts.

The lip is large and cylindrical, purplish-brown, shading to yellowish-green basally.

Ventral sepal is smaller than the dorsal but similar in shape and colouring.

The staminode is creamish-green with brown marbling, and bears three brown markings on its lower margin. It is widely ovate with a wide lower incisure forming two lateral lobes.

Flowers in spring and summer.
Warm conditions.

P. leucochilum (Rolfe) Fowl. 1975 (O.D.)

Subgenus *Brachypetalum* 2n = 26
Malaya: Gulf of Phuket, Krabi, west of Isthmus of Kra.

Previously known as *P. gode-froyae* var. *leucochilum*, this species is found growing in limestone crevices at low elevations around the Gulf of Phuket Krabi on the western coast of Malaya.

The leaves are the same as in *P. godefroyae* and the flowers almost identical except for having larger and brighter red spots.

The staminode is distinctly different to that of *P. godefroyae* and a spur deformity often occurs on the bottom of the lip.

Flowers in summer.
Warm conditions.

P. linii Schoser 1966

Subgenus *Otopedilum*. Section XIII *Spatho-petalum*
Sarawak, north Borneo.

Found growing as an epiphyte in swamps on the roots of mangrove trees. It is of dwarf habit and closely related to *P. bullenianum*.

Leaves are 7 cm (3 in) long and 3 cm ($1\frac{1}{4}$ in) wide. Very light whitish-green with darker green tessellation.

The flower scape is up to 40 cm (16 in) tall, purplish-green, with dense purple down.

The dorsal sepal is rounded and tapers to an acute point. It is light green with darker green veining, hirsute on rear surface, and has re-curved margins.

Petals are very slightly twisted, outspread, and spatulate. Greenish basally, blending into pink before reaching the tips. The mid-vein bears a faint brownish streak which fades out before reaching the tips. The upper margins bear a few brown warts basally and a few brownish-purple spots appear on the lower half of the basal sections.

The lip is whitish-green basally, darkening to a tawny-beige towards the aperture, which has a light green margin.

Ventral sepal is green, narrower than the dorsal, re-curving basally, and tapering to an acute tip.

The staminode is oval, whitish, with green markings in centre section. It is narrow, with prominent upper and lower incisures, the lower of which is much deeper than the upper.

This species is one of the very few which are intolerant of strong air movement and should be grown in a draught-free section of the glass-house.

Flowers in winter.
Warm conditions.

P. lowii (Lindl.) Stein 1847

Subgenus *Otopedilum*. Section VI *Pardalopetalum* 2n = 26 (*Cyp. lowii* Lindl., *Cyp. cruciforme* Zoll & Mir.)
Java, Sarawak, Sulawesi, west Malaya, Sumatra, Kalimantan.

Usually found growing near the sea as epiphytes in tall ironbark trees at elevations of 1000 to 1300 metres (3300 to 4200 feet).

Leaves are pale green, untessellated, notched at the tips, about 25 cm (10 in) long and 3 cm ($1\frac{1}{4}$ in) wide.

The flower scape is up to 70 cm (28 in) tall, and bears from two to six flowers which are up to 10 cm (4 in) wide. It is pubescent, and varies from brownish-purple to green.

The dorsal sepal is oval, narrowing towards the base, and with an acutely pointed apex which bends forward. It is pale yellowish-green with purplish-brown striations.

Petals are long, outspread, curved downwards, and have a single twist. They are yellow, bear purple spots towards the base, and turn to rose-pink towards the tips.

The lip is purple and tinged with green. The in-folded side-lobes are lighter and bear brownish spots.

The ventral sepal is light green with darker veining and is much larger than the dorsal.

The staminode is light yellow with a brownish centre and is fringed with hairs. It is of inverted cordate shape, with a wide and rounded lower incisure which forms two lateral in-pointing lobes.

Flowers in spring and summer.
Warm conditions.

P. mastersianum (Rchb.f.) Stein 1879

Subgenus *Otopedilum*. Section *Mastersianum* Fowl. 2n = 32, 36 (*Cyp. mastersianum* Rchb.f.)
Moluccas: Ambon and Ceram.

Leaves up to 25 cm (10 in) long, dark green with lighter green tessellation.

The flower scape is purple, hirsute, up to 35 cm (14 in) tall, and bears a single flower about 8 cm (3 in) wide.

The dorsal sepal is almost round, bright green with creamish-white margins, and bearing dark green vertical veins. The margins are ciliate.

Petals are copperish-brown, spreading horizontally, undulate on upper margins, and with both margins ciliate. They are paler basally, where small blackish-purple warts are borne along the mid-vein and upper margin.

The lip is very large and pale reddish-brown in colour. The in-folded side-lobes are greenish-brown and spotted with purple.

Ventral sepal is much smaller than the dorsal and is light green with slightly darker green veins.

The staminode is vertically oval, whitish-yellow, with a very large lower incisure forming two prominent in-pointing lobes.

Flowers in spring.
Warm conditions.

P. micranthum Tang & Wang 1951

Subgenus *Otopedilum*. Section XI *Cymatopetalum*
China: south-east Yunnan.

This species is unique among the eastern Asiatic members of *Paphiopedilum*. It can be readily distinguished from all others by its dwarf stature and flower which closely resembles a *Cypripidium*.

A terrestrial erect plant having a greatly elongated rhizome with thick and hairy roots.

Leaves are four to five in number, oblong or strap shaped with blunted tips; leathery, with heavily spotted undersides.

The flower scape is erect, only 4 cm ($1\frac{1}{2}$ in) tall, single flowered and densely clothed with rigid brown hairs.

The bract is rounded, hooded, with a blunted apex, and clothed externally with hairs as on the scape; it is three times as long as the ovary.

The dorsal sepal is ovate with ciliate margins, about 2.5 cm (1 in) long and 1.8 cm ($\frac{3}{4}$ in) wide.

The petals are rounded and about 3 cm ($1\frac{1}{4}$ in) wide.

The lip is elliptical-ovate, 5 cm (2 in) long and 4 cm ($1\frac{1}{2}$ in) wide.

The staminode is rounded underneath and bears a thick fleshy, triangular protuberance with a small divided basal section 3 mm ($\frac{1}{8}$ in) long.

NOTE: The original Latin description by Tang and Wang contains many words which do not appear in available books on taxonomy and Latin diagnoses. Rather than guess at the meaning of these words, the sections containing them have been omitted and the above description is therefore brief and subject to correction.

P. moquetteanum (J.J.Sm.) Fowl. 1905 (O.D.)

P. victoria-regina (Sander) M. W. Wood subsp. *glaucophyllum* (J.J.Sm.) M. W. Wood var. *moquetteanum* (J.J.Sm.) M. W. Wood, *comb. nov.* 1976 (O.R.)

Subgenus *Otopedilum*. Section VII *Cochlopetalum*. 2n = 34
West Java: Bogor.

Leaves and flower scape are the same as in the subspecies *glaucophyllum*.

The dorsal sepal is yellowish-green and hooded at the apex. It has no white margin but is striated with rows of purplish-brown dots.

Petals are twisted, undulate, and ciliate on both margins. White in colour, with scattered, longitudinal, purplish-red markings. Width across the petals is up to 11 cm ($4\frac{1}{2}$ in).

The lip is a solid rose-pink except for a few small purplish dots near the 'toe'. The aperture margin is white.

Ventral sepal is smaller than the dorsal but similar in colour.

The staminode is rhombic in shape and is concave basally. The upper section is pale yellowish-green, changing to a deep reddish-purple basally.

Flowers in summer.
Warm conditions.

P. nigritum (Rchb.f.) Stein 1882

Subgenus *Otopedilum*. Section XIV *Blepharopetalum* (*Cyp. nigritum* Rchb.f.) Borneo: Mt Kinabalu.

Found growing at elevations of 1300 to 1500 metres (4200 to 5000 feet).

Leaves are dark green with lighter tessellation and have three distinct teeth at their tips. They are 14 cm ($5\frac{1}{2}$ in) long, and 3 cm ($1\frac{1}{4}$ in) wide, keeled, and silvery-green on their undersides.

The flower scape is brownish-purple, up to 20 cm (8 in) tall, and bears a single flower about 8 cm (3 in) wide.

The dorsal sepal is broad, acutely pointed, and recurved basally. It is white with vertical striations which are greenish basally and shade upwards to purple. The margins are flushed with rose-purple.

Petals are greenish basally, becoming brownish-red towards the tips and bearing a few dark warts. Margins are undulate and hirsute.

The lip is brownish-purple veined with darker brown.

Ventral sepal is about the same size as the dorsal but is light green with darker green veins.

The staminode is yellow with whitish margins, very widely ovate.

Flowers in spring and summer.

Warm conditions.

P. niveum (Rchb.f.) Stein 1869

Subgenus *Brachypetalum* 2n = 26 Malay Arch., Langkawi Is., Satoon, Thailand.

Found growing close to the sea, in crevices of limestone rock, and it is reported as being subject to salt spray.

It is a dwarf growing species with small obtusely pointed leaves. They are dark green, mottled with grey on upper surfaces, and dull red beneath.

The flower scape is short and purplish, rarely exceeding 12 cm (5 in) in height. Flowers are usually single but sometimes appear in pairs.

The dorsal sepal is almost circular, about 7 cm (3 in) wide. It is white, with very fine purple spotting basally, and bears purple streaks on the reverse side.

Petals are rounded, white, with a sprinkling of very small purplish spots basally.

The lip is small and ovate. White, with minute purple spots.

Ventral sepal is very small and similar in colour to the other segments.

The staminode is white with yellow markings in its centre.

Flowers in spring and summer.

Warm conditions.

P. papuanum Ridl. 1915

Subgenus *Otopedilum*. Section XIV *Blepharopetalum* (*Cyp. papuanum* Ridl.)
West Irian: Mt Carstenz.

Found growing at an elevation of 800 metres (about 2600 feet), this species has leaves 8 to 10 cm (3 to 4 in) long, green, tessellated, and acutely pointed.

The dorsal sepal is green with crimson-magenta veining.

Petals are dull crimson with darker spotting basally, tinged with greenish-yellow, and with ciliate margins.

The lip is dull crimson with greenish-yellow lobes.

No formal description or illustration of this species is currently available.

Warm conditions.

P. parishii (Rchb.f.) Stein 1869

Subgenus *Otopedilum*. Section V *Mystropetalum* 2n = 26 (*Cyp. parishii* Rchb.f.)
Burma, Thailand.

Found growing as an epiphyte at an elevation of 1200 metres (about 4000 feet), this species has a very similar plant habit to that of *P. philippinense*.

Leaves are long and leathery, 30 to 50 cm (12 to 20 in) long and 5 cm (2 in) wide, and have an obliquely rounded tip. They are untessellated and the upper surfaces are darker than the undersides.

The flower scape is up to 50 cm (20 in) tall, thick, branched, and hirsute. Pale green in colour, and bearing from four to six flowers.

The dorsal sepal is broad and bent forward. Rich cream in colour, veined with pale green.

Petals are up to 12 cm (5 in) long, undulate, twisted, and pendulous. Green basally, turning to a reddish-purple apically, and having purple, hairy warts on both margins.

The lip is large and elongated, deep green tinged with purple.

Ventral sepal is smaller than the dorsal but otherwise similar.

The staminode is pale yellow marbled with green, similar in shape to an elongated arrow-head.

Flowers in spring and summer.

Warm conditions.

P. philippinense (Rchb.f.) Stein 1862

Subgenus *Anotopedilum*. Section III *Coryopedilum* 2n = 26 (*Cyp. philippinense* Rchb.f.)
Philippines: Guimares, Mindanao, Palawan to north Borneo.

Found growing in brightly lit positions near the coast, usually as an epiphyte.

Leaves up to 30 cm (12 in) long, strap shaped, leathery, bright green, glossy, and untessellated.

Flower scape up to 40 cm (16 in) tall, hirsute, bearing up to five large flowers.

Dorsal sepal is tall and broad, bending forward, white with purple stripes, and pubescent on rear surface.

The petals are up to 15 cm (6 in) long, very narrow, pendulous, and slightly twisted. They are yellow basally, green at mid-length, and almost white at the tips. The mid-section is heavily blotched with brown. Both margins bear hairy warts basally.

The lip is small, tawny-yellow, and veined with green.

The ovary is sheathed for half its length with a reddish-brown, hairy bract.

Ventral sepal is white with green veining and is slightly smaller than the dorsal.

The staminode is cordate, convex, creamy-white with green veining, and fringed with blackish hairs on each side margin.

Flowers in summer and autumn.

Warm conditions.

P. praestans (Rchb.f.) Stein 1886

Subgenus *Anotopedilum*. Section III *Coryopetalum* 2n = 26 (*Cyp. praestans* Rchb.f., *P. glanduliferum* Blume)
Islands west of New Guinea.

Found growing in crevices of limestone rocks.

Leaves up to 50 cm (20 in) long, very leathery, broadly rounded at ends and distinctly keeled. Dark green and untessellated.

Flower scape is up to 50 cm (20 in) tall, blackish-purple, lightly spotted with green. Hirsute and branching, bearing up to four large flowers, 20 cm (8 in) wide and 13 cm (5 in) high.

Dorsal sepal about 5 cm (2 in) high and 3 cm ($1\frac{1}{4}$ in) wide, bending forward over flower. Creamy-white striped with brownish-purple.

Petals are 12 cm ($4\frac{1}{2}$ in) long, twisted spirally and slightly drooping. Golden-green, with stripe of deep brown down the mid-line, and having a series of black spots on the basal margins.

The lip is about 4 cm ($1\frac{1}{2}$ in) long, glossy, pale yellowish-green, and marked with reddish-brown veins.

The ventral sepal is smaller than the dorsal but similar in shape and colour.

The staminode is cordate and distinctly convex.

Flowers in spring and summer.

Warm conditions.

P. purpurascens

P. praestans

P. philippinense

P. purpuratum

P. roebbelenii

P. robinsonii

P. randsii

P. sanderianum

P. rothschildianum

P. spicerianum

P. stonei

P. sublaeve

P. thailandense

P. tonsum

P. urbanianum

P. sukhakulii

P. victoria-mariae

P. venustum

P. villosum

P. violascens

P. virens

P. volonteanum

P. wardii

P. wentworthianum

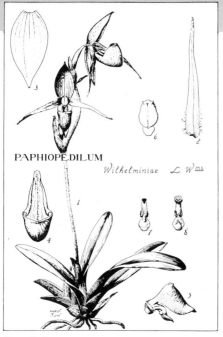

P. wilhelminiae

P. wolterianum

'*P. dayanum*-like' new species

P. zieckianum

P. purpurascens Fowl. 1974

Subgenus *Otopedilum*. Section XIV *Blepharopetalum*
North Borneo: Mt Kinabalu (Sabah).

Leaves 8 to 14 cm (3 to $5\frac{1}{2}$ in) long and 2 to 4 cm ($1\frac{1}{4}$ to $1\frac{1}{2}$ in) wide. Narrowly elliptical, mid-green, tessellated with darker green.

Flower scape up to 14 cm ($5\frac{1}{2}$ in) tall, densely clothed with short hairy bristles.

The dorsal sepal has reflexed basal margins and in-turned upper margins. It is broadly ovate-elliptical, sharply pointed apically, 4 cm ($1\frac{1}{2}$ in) high, and 3.5 cm ($1\frac{1}{4}$ in) wide. Whitish-green with dark green vertical striations.

Petals are obtuse, slightly drooping, and pointed apically, 4.5 cm ($1\frac{3}{4}$ in) long and 1.5 cm ($\frac{1}{2}$ in) wide. Both margins bear small raised warts and a few hairy bristles basally. The basal two-thirds are deep green, shading to a deep lavender-purple towards the tips.

The lip is bluntly obtuse, 4 to 5 cm ($1\frac{1}{2}$ to 2 in) long, and 2 to 3 cm ($\frac{3}{4}$ to $1\frac{1}{4}$ in) wide. Greenish-brown, lightening towards the base.

Ventral sepal is of the same colouring but narrower and shorter.

The staminode is about 1.5 cm ($\frac{1}{2}$ in) wide, suborbicular, greenish, with darker green veins. The upper incisure is triangular and 3 mm ($\frac{1}{8}$ in) deep. The lower incisure is a compound cleft forming lateral lobes.

Flowers in summer.

Warm conditions.

P. purpuratum (Lindl.) Stein 1837

Subgenus *Otopedilum*. Section XIV *Blepharopetalum* 2n = 40, 48 (*Cyp. purpuratum* Lindl., *Cyp. sinicum*. Hance)
Hong Kong and adjacent Chinese coast.

Leaves about 12 cm (5 in) long, pale green with deeper green tessellation.

Flower scape up to 17 cm (7 in) long bearing a single flower about 8 cm (3 in) wide.

The dorsal sepal is large and broad, folded at mid-vein. White, with a greenish stain centrally, and bearing small blackish warts basally.

Petals are spreading and slightly undulate. Purplish-crimson with dark purple veins. Green basally and with ciliate margins. The basal sections bear numerous small blackish warts.

The lip is brownish-purple with darker veins. In-folded side-lobes are light purple and bear many small glistening warts.

Ventral sepal is smaller than the dorsal and light green in colour.

The staminode is whitish-green, stained with purple at the margins. Inverted, heart-shaped, with a wide lower incisure forming in-pointed lateral lobes.

Flowers in winter.

Intermediate conditions.

P. randsii Fowl. 1969

Subgenus *Anotopedilum*. Section III *Coryopedilum* 2n = 26
Philippines: Northern end of Mindanao Is.

An epiphyte which grows in dense shade at an elevation of 500 metres (1600 feet), this species resembles *P. philippinense* but has shorter petals.

Leaves are 30 to 38 cm (12 to 15 in) long and 5 to 6 cm (2 to $2\frac{1}{2}$ in) wide. Keeled, untessellated, pale green with yellowed margins.

The flower scape is erect and reaches 45 cm (18 in) in height. Reddish-brown, hirsute, and bearing three to five flowers.

Dorsal sepal is creamish, veined with dark purple, 3 to 5 cm (1 to 2 in) in height.

The petals are pendulous, narrow, 7 to 10 cm ($2\frac{3}{4}$ to 4 in) long, light yellow with greenish veins.

The lip is helmet-shaped with an indentation at the 'toe'. It is yellow with greenish veins.

Ventral sepal is smaller than the dorsal but similar in shape and colour.

The staminode is creamy-white veined with green. Concave with ciliate margins.

Flowers in summer.

Warm conditions.

P. robinsonii (Ridl.) Ridl. 1915

Subgenus *Otopedilum*. Section XIII *Spathopetalum*
Malaya: Mt Tahan.

A small compact plant found growing at elevations of 1300 to 1800 metres (4200 to 6000 feet). It grows in deep, wet moss, in heavily shaded positions, and sometimes sends out long runners on which new plants form.

Leaves are ovate, 7 to 9 cm ($2\frac{3}{4}$ to $3\frac{1}{2}$ in) long and 3 cm ($1\frac{1}{4}$ in) wide. They are light green, tessellated with a lighter, silvery-green.

The flower scape is about 30 cm (12 in) tall, erect, and bears a single flower about 6 cm ($2\frac{1}{2}$ in) in height.

The dorsal sepal arches forward from the base with upper margin curved forward and lower side margins reflexed. It is broadly ovate with a keeled apex. Light green suffused basally with mauve, and having a purple median line extending from the base almost to the apex.

The petals are narrow basally, widening towards mid-length and then tapering to a pointed apex. Upper margins are undulate and bear brownish-purple spots. Yellowish-green basally turning to a mauve-pink towards the tips.

The lip is large, yellowish-green, with deeper green veins basally. Ranging upwards from the 'toe', the colour changes to a brownish-yellow.

Ventral sepal is ovate, smaller than the dorsal sepal, and pale green in colour.

The staminode is cordate and notched at the apex. Yellowish-brown with a whitish centre, surrounded with greenish-purple veins. This species is the only member of the *Spathopetalum* section having a cordate-shaped staminode.

Flowers in summer.

Warm conditions.

P. roebbelenii (Rchb.f.) 1883 (O.D.)

P. philippinense var. *roebbelenii* (Rchb.f.) Kerchove (O.R.)

Subgenus *Anotopedilum*. Section III *Coryopedilum* 2n = 26
Philippines: Samar Is.; Cebu.

Very similar to *P. philippinense* but is slightly smaller, has a more verrucose ('warty') staminode, and petals which are more pendulous and twisted.

Leaves are 23 to 28 cm (9 to 11 in) long and 3.5 cm ($1\frac{1}{2}$ in) wide, pro-minently keeled, and with dentate tips. Mid-green, untessellated, and of leathery texture.

The flower scape is 20 to 26 cm (8 to 10 in) long and bears many flowers. It is reddish-brown, hirsute, and branching.

The dorsal sepal is 4 cm ($1\frac{3}{4}$ in) high and 2.5 cm (1 in) wide, narrowly ovate, with slightly undulate margins. White, suffused with light green basally and at tip, and bearing about nine brownish stripes.

Petals are narrow, pendulous, and twisted. About 10 cm (4 in) long and 0.5 cm ($\frac{1}{4}$ in) wide. Light green basally with a few maroon spots. The remainder is heavily striped with maroon. Pubescent on both surfaces.

The lip is 1.5 cm ($\frac{1}{2}$ in) wide and 3 cm ($1\frac{1}{4}$ in) long. Greenish-yellow with brown veining, with in-folded side-lobes which meet.

Ventral sepal is smaller than the dorsal but similar in shape and colour. In some plants of this species, this segment reverts to its primeval ancestors and deforms into two separate 'lateral' sepals.

The ovary is very hirsute and sheathed with a striped bract of the same colouring as the sepals.

The staminode is cordate, convex, ciliate, with many small self-coloured warts. It is creamy with green marbling.

Flowers in summer.

Warm conditions.

P. rothschildianum (Rchb.f.) Stein 1888

Subgenus *Anotopedilum*. Section II *Gonatopetalum* 2n = 26, 28 (*Cyp. rothschildianum* Rchb.f., *Cyp. neo-guinense* Lindl.)
North Borneo (Sabah): Mt Kinabalu.

Found growing on mountainsides at an elevation of 1000 metres (3300 feet).

Leaves are very long and lustrous, up to 60 cm ($23\frac{1}{2}$ in) long and 5 cm (2 in) wide.

The flower scape is robust, hirsute, reddish, up to 60 cm (24 in) tall, and bears two to five flowers up to 12 cm (5 in) in height.

The dorsal sepal is long, 'pinched', pointed at the apex, pale yellowish-white, and with a white margin. It has purplish-black vertical striations.

Petals are long, narrow, twisted apically, and have undulate basal margins. They are creamy-yellow with longitudinal lines of dark brown spots.

The lip is large and of heavy texture, cinnamon brown with darker brown veining, and with a prominent median vein.

The ventral sepal is slightly shorter than the dorsal but similar in shape and colour.

Flowers in summer.

Warm conditions.

P. sanderianum (Rchb.f.) Stein 1886

Subgenus *Anotopedilum*. Section III *Coryopedilum*
North Borneo: Sabah.

Leaves thick and leathery, keeled, up to 40 cm (16 in) long, dark green and untessellated.

Flower scape is up to 50 cm (20 in) tall. Stout, pubescent, dark purple, and bearing three to five flowers about 10 cm (4 in) in height.

The dorsal sepal is triangular in shape, concave, hirsute and keeled, yellowish-green, with broad vertical, brownish stripes.

Petals are up to 50 cm (20 in) long, pendulous, twisted, and ciliate. Pale yellow bordered with brownish-purple for the basal 8 cm (3 in), then spotted with brownish-purple for half their length. The remaining apical section is dull purple with scattered bars and dots.

The lip is brownish-purple frontally and pale yellow on the back surface.

Ventral sepal is similar to the dorsal in shape and colour but is much smaller.

The staminode is pale yellow with purple markings and has ciliate margins.

Warm conditions.

P. schmidtianum Krzl. 1902

Subgenus *Otopedilum*. Section XV *Phacopetalum*
Gulf of Thailand: Island of Koh Chang.

No description or illustration of this lost species is available.

P. spicerianum (Rchb.f.) Stein 1880

Subgenus *Otopedilum*. Section XI *Cymatopetalum* 2n = 28, 30 (*Cyp. spicerianum* Rchb.f.)
India: Barak and Sonai gorges, Silchar district.

Found growing at elevations of 700 to 1300 metres (2300 to 4200 feet) in rock crevices among grass and ferns.

Leaves are 20 cm (8 in) long and 2 cm ($\frac{3}{4}$ in) wide, dark green and untessellated. Spotted basally on undersides with rich purple.

The flower scape is up to 22 cm (9 in) tall, purple, and finely pubescent.

Dorsal sepal is 6 cm ($2\frac{1}{2}$ in) wide, narrow basally and terminating apically in two, large, rounded lobes. It is reflexed basally, with the sidelobes bent forward to form a hood. The basal section is bright green and the remainder snowy white. A wide and distinctive purple stripe runs vertically from base to apex.

Petals are 4 cm ($1\frac{1}{2}$ in) long, slightly drooping, curved forward, and have distinct undulate margins. Pale yellowish-green with a prominent purplish mid-line.

The lip is large, very wide, light brown, flushed with purple.

Ventral sepal is very light green, broadly ovate, smaller than the dorsal, with a keeled and acute tip.

The staminode is most distinctive, being convoluted and of a shape unlike that of any other *Paphiopedilum*. It is white with rosy-purple markings.

Flowers in autumn.
Cool conditions.

P. stonei (Hk.f.) Stein 1862

Subgenus *Anotopedilum*. Section IV *Prenipedilum* 2n = 26 (*Cyp. stonei* Hk.f.)
Borneo: Sarawak.

Found growing on rocks in semi-shaded positions at elevations of 300 to 500 metres (1000 to 1600 feet).

Leaves are strap-shaped, leathery, bright green and untessellated. They are up to 38 cm (15 in) long and 3 cm ($1\frac{1}{4}$ in) wide.

The flower scape is up to 60 cm (24 in) tall, dull greenish-purple, pubescent, and bears three to five flowers.

The dorsal sepal is large and of inverted heart-shape. It is creamy white in colour, is keeled, tapers to an acute point, and usually bears about 16 blackish-crimson vertical stripes.

The petals are 12 to 15 cm (5 to 6 in) long, pendulous and twisted, with a few black hairs on each margin. Pale yellow in colour, spotted with reddish-brown.

The lip is large and has the distinctive habit of projecting forward at an angle of 45 degrees. It is a dull rose-pink, veined with crimson, and has a creamish-white underside. The side-lobes are white and in-folded.

Ventral sepal is similar in colour to the dorsal but slightly smaller and more deeply keeled.

The staminode is yellowish-white, fringed with bristle-like hairs, and bends sharply outwards and downwards.

Flowers in summer and autumn.
Warm conditions.

P. sublaeve (Rchb.f.) Fowl. 1888

Subgenus *Otopedilum*. Section XV *Phacopetalum* 2n = 57 (*Cyp. callosum* var. *sublaeve*)
Western Malaysia: Kedah Peak.

The leaves of this species are identical to those of *P. callosum* and the flower is very similar. However, the flower scapes are shorter, almost always bear at least two flowers which have brighter red markings on all segments, and have petals with upturned tips.

Flowers in summer.
Warm conditions.

NOTE: This species was renamed *P. birkii* in 1984.

P. sukhakulii Schoser & Senghas 1965

Subgenus *Otopedilum*. Section *Venustum* Fowl. 2n = 40
North-east Thailand.

Usually found growing alongside shaded streams at an elevation of 1000 metres (3300 feet) although sometimes found growing with *P. callosum* at lower altitudes.

Leaves are up to 25 cm (10 in) long and 5 cm (2 in) wide. Light green with darker green tessellation. The undersides are of smoother texture and are more faintly tessellated.

The flower scape is up to 22 cm (9 in) tall, dark purplish-brown, and covered with fine, light-green hairs.

The dorsal sepal is acutely pointed and in-folded for the apical 1 cm ($\frac{1}{2}$ in). It is 3 to 4 cm ($1\frac{1}{4}$ to $1\frac{1}{2}$ in) wide and 4 to 5 cm ($1\frac{1}{2}$ to 2 in) in height. White, or very light whitish-green, with about 18 vertical green stripes. The basal sections of these stripes are spotted with purplish-red. Lower margins are sparsely haired.

Petals are horizontal, 12 to 16 cm ($4\frac{3}{4}$ to $6\frac{1}{2}$ in) across, sharply pointed and slightly wider at mid-length. Green in colour, lightening to yellowish-white apically. Densely spotted with purplish-red, the spots diminish in size towards the tips. Both margins bear hairs of the same colour as the spots.

The lip is helmet-shaped, 3 cm ($1\frac{1}{4}$ in) wide and 4 cm ($1\frac{1}{2}$ in) long. Light green with purplish veining frontally. Upper sections of the lobes are in-folded, glistening, deep reddish-purple with raised warts.

Ventral sepal is the same length as the dorsal but narrower and more acutely pointed.

The staminode is rounded and about 1 cm ($\frac{1}{2}$ in) in diameter. Very light green with deeper green veining centrally. The lower margin bears two large incisures which form three prominent 'teeth'.

Flowers in winter.

Warm conditions.

P. superbiens (Rchb.f.) Stein 1855

Subgenus *Otopedilum*. Section XV *Phacopetalum* (*Cyp. superbiens* Rchb.f., *Cyp. veitchianum* Lindl.)
Islands of Malacca Straits, Java, Assam.

Leaves about 15 cm (6 in) long and 5 cm (2 in) wide, rounded apically, pale yellowish-green, beautifully tessellated with dull dark-green.

The flower scape is up to 30 cm (12 in) long, purplish, pubescent, and bearing a single flower.

The dorsal sepal is large and broad, terminating in a sharply 'pinched' apex. White, evenly striped with green and deep reddish-purple. The side margins are re-curved basally.

The petals are pendulous, 7 cm (3 in) long and 2 cm ($\frac{3}{4}$ in) wide. White, veined with green, fringed with hairs on both margins, and bearing many small blackish spots which extend almost to the tips.

The lip is very large, brownish-purple frontally, and pale green on back surfaces. The in-folded side lobes are warty and flushed with crimson.

Ventral sepal is about half the size of the dorsal, acutely pointed, whitish-green, striped with darker green.

The staminode is light whitish-green, veined with darker green. The lower margin has two prominent lateral teeth which project lower than the smaller central tooth.

NOTE: This species is described by M. W. Wood and P. J. Cribb as *P. superbiens* subsp. *superbiens*. (*Curtis's Botanical Magazine*, 1981.)

P. thailandense Hort. ex Fowl. 1981

Subgenus *Otopedilum*. Sub-section *Barbatum-Callosum* (formerly *Phacopetalum*) Central Thailand: Isthmus of Kra Mountains.

This newly discovered species has not yet been formally described. It resembles the form of *P. barbatum* found in western Malaysia and is very closely related to *P. sublaeve*.

P. tonsum (Rchb.f.) Stein 1883

Subgenus *Otopedilum*. Section XIV *Blepharopetalum* (*Cyp. tonsum* Rchb.f.) Sumatra.

This species, together with its many different subspecies, is found growing in dense shade at elevations of 500 to 1000 metres (1600 to 3300 feet), in areas subject to very high humidity and rainfall.

Leaves are 12 to 16 cm ($4\frac{3}{4}$ to $6\frac{1}{2}$ in) long and 3 cm ($1\frac{1}{4}$ in) wide. Pointed, light green tessellated with darker green, undersides spotted basally with purple.

The flower scape is erect, 30 to 45 cm (12 to 18 in) tall, dull purplish-green, and bears a single flower about 9 cm ($3\frac{1}{2}$ in) wide.

The dorsal sepal is creamy-white and folded at mid-vein. It is evenly striped with green, each alternate stripe being shorter and tinged with purple. The margins are ciliate.

Petals are broad and spreading, pale green with darker green veins which are sometimes stained with purple. They bear a few black hairs towards the tip, three to five blackish warts along the mid-vein, and a few smaller warts along the upper margin.

The lip is large and helmet-shaped, dull green, tinged with brown and red. The in-folded side-lobes almost meet and are brown and warty.

Ventral sepal is smaller than the dorsal but similar in shape and colouring.

The staminode is a very pale whitish-green and has a glossy green uvula, projecting downwards from the centre of its lower margin.

Flowers in autumn.

Warm conditions.

P. urbanianum Fowl. 1981

Subgenus *Otopedilum*. Section XV *Phacopetalum*. 2n = 36 Philippines: Mindoro.

This newly discovered species is closely related to *P. fowliei, P. argus*, and *P. hennisianum*. It is found growing at elevations of 500 to 800 metres (1600 to 2600 feet), usually as a semi-terrestrial, but more rarely as a semi-epiphyte on the bases of trees amongst rocky outcrops.

Leaves are 12 to 20 cm ($4\frac{3}{4}$ to 8 in) long, and 3 to 4 cm ($1\frac{1}{4}$ to $1\frac{1}{2}$ in) wide, narrowly elliptic with toothed apices. They are dark green with irregular darker mottling.

The flower scape reaches 25 cm (10 in) in height, is densely haired and bears one or two flowers.

The dorsal sepal projects forward slightly, and is broadly elliptic with an acutely pointed apex. It is about 3 cm ($1\frac{1}{4}$ in) in height and width, white, with 11 to 13 vertical green striations almost identical to *P. hennisianum*. Some clones carry a slight pinkish tinge laterally.

The petals are about 6 cm ($2\frac{1}{2}$ in) long and 1 cm ($\frac{1}{2}$ in) wide, spreading, drooping at an angle of about 30 degrees, and bearing a half-twist towards the apices. Green basally, with about eight longitudinal veins which fade at about mid-length into the lavender-pink distal section. About 12 warts, bearing one to three short hairs, are borne on the upper margin basally and rows of smaller, but more numerous, warts adorn the mid-line and lower margins basally.

The labellum is 4.5 cm ($1\frac{3}{4}$ in) long and 2.5 cm (1 in) wide, narrowing only slightly below the aperture. It is greenish-brown with darker veining.

The ventral sepal is the same length as the dorsal but slightly narrower and it bears about nine vertical green striations on a whitish ground.

The staminode is vertically oval, about 1 cm ($\frac{1}{2}$ in) wide and 1.3 cm ($\frac{5}{8}$ in) in height. It has a single cleft on the upper margin with a deeper notch on the lower margin provided with a small uvula. The segment is light yellowish-green with a prominent and distinctive filigree pattern of darker green, and is clothed with minute hairs.

Flowers in spring.

Warm conditions.

P. venustum (Wall.) Stein 1820

Subgenus *Otopedilum*. Section *Venustum* Fowl. 2n = 40, 41 (*Cyp. venustum* Wall.) Nepal, Assam.

Found growing in warm and sheltered valleys at elevations of 1000 to 1500 metres (3300 to 5000 feet).

Leaves are elliptic to strap-shaped, pointed, 12 cm ($4\frac{3}{4}$ in) long and 3 cm ($1\frac{1}{4}$ in) wide. They are velvety, dark green mottled with greyish-green on upper surfaces, with the undersides heavily mottled with dull purple. They have a pronounced keel.

The flower scape is erect, up to 25 cm (10 in) tall, and bears a single flower up to 6 cm ($2\frac{1}{2}$ in) in height.

The dorsal sepal is white, veined with dark green, broad, and acutely pointed.

The petals are spreading, recurved, spatulate, and slightly twisted. Green basally, with blackish warts at mid-vein and near the margins. Tips are dull purple, tinged with brown. Both margins bear long stiff hairs.

The lip is pale yellowish-orange, tinged with rose-pink and veined with green. The in-folded side-lobes almost meet and are tawny brownish-green.

The ventral sepal is small, narrow, and pale green with darker green veins.

The staminode is light greenish-yellow with brownish-red markings in its central area. It is slightly cupped, with a small, central, basal tooth.

Flowers in winter.

Cool conditions.

P. victoria-mariae (Rolfe) Hooker 1896 (O.D.)

P. victoria-regina (Sander) M. W. Wood, *comb. nov.* 1967 (O.R.)

Subgenus *Otopedilum*. Section VII *Cochlopetalum*
Central Sumatra: Padang.

Found growing at an elevation of 2000 metres (6600 feet), this species has leaves 30 to 40 cm (12 to 16 in) long and 5 to 6 cm (2 to $2\frac{1}{2}$ in) wide. They are dull green, very faintly tessellated, and are ciliate basally. The undersides are paler and flushed basally with purple. The margins and mid-veins are slightly darker.

The flower scape is up to 60 cm (24 in) tall, dark purplish-brown, densely hirsute, and bears up to eight flowers which are about 7 cm (3 in) wide.

The dorsal sepal is almost circular and white to pale creamish-yellow. It has a light green central area which is sometimes marked with very faint green striations. Margins are ciliate and undulate.

Petals are spreading horizontally, twisted, undulate, and have ciliate margins. They are pale green, flushed with purple basally, sometimes with very faint purplish lines, but lack the predominant dark-purplish-red lines and bars peculiar to the other members of the same section.

Also the lip is light pink and more slender than in other members. The aperture has a whitish margin.

The ventral sepal is smaller than the dorsal and has no white margin.

The staminode is quite different to that of other *Cochlopetalum* species. It is basically rhombic in shape, with the lower part tapering to an elongated point. Its upper section is convex, while the lower, tapering section is concave.

Many plants imported as *P. victoria-mariae* are in fact *P. chamberlainianum* var. *latifolia*.

Flowers in spring and summer.
Warm conditions.

P. villosum (Lindl.) Stein 1854

Subgenus *Otopedilum*. Section IX *Neuropetalum* 2n = 26 (*Cyp. villosum* Lindl.)
Assam, Burma, Thailand, and Laos.

Found growing in tangled masses of mosses and decaying leaves at elevations of 1200 to 1600 metres (4000 to 5200 feet). It has been reported as sometimes growing as an epiphyte.

The leaves are leathery, 25 to 35 cm (10 to 14 in) long and 3 cm ($1\frac{1}{4}$ in) wide. Bright green above, paler underneath, and spotted with purple basally. The upper surfaces are very faintly mottled.

The flower scape is normally green, hirsute, and up to 30 cm (12 in) tall. It bears a single and very highly glazed flower up to 12 cm (5 in) wide. Another less common form bearing identical flowers has a distinctive reddish-purple scape.

The dorsal sepal is broadly ovate and fringed with hairs. It is narrow basally and hooded apically, bearing a hairy keel on the back surface. The lower section is brownish-purple, the remainder green with a white margin. The green section bears brownish-purple vertical striations.

The petals are fringed with fine hairs and are spatulate, undulate, and bent forward. The upper half is yellowish-brown, separated from the slightly paler lower section by a distinct brownish-purple mid-vein.

The lip is large and brownish-yellow, with a lighter yellow margin around the aperture. The in-folded side-lobes are broad and tawny-yellow with the whole segment having a glossy, 'varnished' appearance.

The ventral sepal is the same length as the dorsal but much narrower.

The staminode is oval, glistening deep yellow, with a prominent green tubercle at lower centre.

Flowers in autumn.
Cool conditions.

P. violascens Schltr. 1911

Subgenus *Otopedilum*. Section XIV *Blepharopetalum* 2n = 38
New Guinea: Kar-Kar Is., Garaina and Kui areas.

Found growing in dense shade at elevations of 900 to 1000 metres (3000 to 3300 feet), sometimes as an epiphyte.

The leaves are greyish-green mottled with darker green, keeled, 12 to 20 cm (5 to 8 in) long and up to 3 cm ($1\frac{1}{4}$ in) wide.

The flower scape is dark brown,

hirsute, 13 to 24 cm (5 to $9\frac{1}{2}$ in) tall, and bears a single flower 5 to 7 cm (2 to 3 in) wide.

The dorsal sepal is blush-pink with a greenish margin fringed with short hairs. It bears reddish-purple veins and has a slightly hooded apex.

The petals are wide, magenta-purple basally, shading to pink, then to white at the tips, and striped with parallel purple veins. Below the horizontal mid-line is a small white area which extends from the point of attachment to almost mid-length.

The lip is large, helmet-shaped, khaki in colour, lightening to dark olive-green towards the 'toe', and has in-folded, glossy side-lobes.

The ventral sepal is lighter in colour than the dorsal and much smaller.

The staminode is horizontally oval with a wide lower incisure forming two lateral lobes. In the centre of the incisure is a small pendant uvula.

Flowers in early summer.

Warm conditions.

P. virens (Rchb.f.) Stein 1863

Subgenus *Otopedilum*. Section XIV *Blepharopetalum* 2n = 40 (*Cyp. virens.* Rchb.f.)
North Borneo: Mt Kinabalu.

Once considered to be a variety of *P. javanicum*, it is closely allied to that species. The main differences are in the shape of the staminodes, intensity of colour, and the much lighter green foliage of *P. virens*.

In all segments of the flower the green colouration is deeper and brighter than in *P. javanicum*.

The petals are spreading and reflexed beyond mid-length.

The lip is deeper, more glossy, and much narrower basally than in *P. javanicum*.

The staminode is wide, pink, with green marbling in the centre, and bears a prominent green glossy tubercle. The upper incisure is V-shaped, while the lower margin bears four distinct incisures.

Flowers in spring.

Warm conditions.

P. volonteanum (Sand.) Stein 1890

Subgenus *Otopedilum*. Section *Hookerae* Fowl. (*Cyp. volonteanum* Sand.)
Borneo: Sabah area.

Leaves are dark green with paler green tessellation, 20 cm (8 in) long and 4 cm ($1\frac{1}{2}$ in) wide.

The flower scape is about 15 cm (6 in) tall, bearing a single flower up to 8 cm (3 in) wide.

The dorsal sepal is oval, tapering to an acute tip, with upper margins curved forwards. Pale yellowish-green lightening apically, and bearing darker green veins.

The petals bend down slightly, are obtuse, spatulate, and have slight undulations basally. Rose-red apically, quickly changing to a whitish-green, then to a deeper green basally. Both margins and the mid-line bear scattered black warts.

The lip is pale green, slightly suffused basally with rose-pink, and turning to brown towards the rim. The in-folded side-lobes are yellowish-green with dark brown spots.

The ventral sepal is smaller than the dorsal but similar in shape and colour.

The staminode is rounded and has no upper incisure. The lower margin bears a widely rounded incisure which forms two lateral lobes. It is brownish-green with a pale yellowish vertical mark on the mid-line.

Flowers in summer and autumn.
Warm conditions.

P. wardii Summerhayes 1932

Subgenus *Otopedilum*. Section *Venustum*
Fowl. 2n = 40
North Burma: Tamai River Valley.

Found growing at elevations of 1200 to 1500 metres (4000 to 5000 feet).

Leaves are 10 to 14 cm (4 to $5\frac{1}{2}$ in) long, 2 to 3 cm ($\frac{3}{4}$ to $1\frac{1}{4}$ in) wide, silvery-green, mottled with darker green on upper surfaces. Undersides are marked with scattered purple dots becoming denser basally. Slightly up-curved and having an apical tooth.

The flower scape is up to 25 cm (10 in) tall, purple, pubescent, and bears a single flower 6 to 7 cm ($2\frac{1}{2}$ to 3 in) wide.

The dorsal sepal is white with green veins rising from the base almost to the apex. Lower section is lightly suffused with rose-purple.

The petals are long, spreading, and slightly drooping, but sometimes with tips slightly up-turned. Their colour is light green basally, changing to brownish-red, with a very short white tip. They bear blackish-purple spotting and striping over most of their surface, and both margins have black hairs.

The lip is chestnut brown with darker reddish-brown veins. Elongated and wedge-shaped, with a marbled pattern.

Ventral sepal is cupped, white, with green veining.

The staminode is rather horseshoe-shaped, 11 mm ($\frac{1}{2}$ in) wide and 8 mm ($\frac{3}{8}$ in) high. Margins are light whitish-green and the central section is marbled with green and chartreuse.

Flowers in winter.
Warm conditions.

P. wentworthianum Schoser & Fowl. 1968

Subgenus *Otopedilum*. Section *Mastersianum* Fowl. 2n = 40
Bougainville Is: Kieta.

Resembling, and closely related to *P. mastersianum* and *P. zieckianum*, this species is found at elevations of 1500 to 2500 metres (5000 to 8200 feet), growing in deep shade under very humid conditions.

Leaves are 11 to 15 cm (4½ to 6 in) long and 3 to 5 cm (1¼ to 2 in) wide, narrowly elliptical, dark green, and slightly tessellated.

The flower scape is only about 10 cm (4 in) in height and bears a single flower.

The dorsal sepal is broad basally, tapering to a very acute tip. The base is whitish, flushed with green and light brown, and has darker green vertical stripes which fade towards the ciliate margins.

The petals are narrow basally, widening towards the tips. They are dark brownish-purple basally, shading to a rich rose shade apically. The margins are slightly undulate.

The lip is light green basally, flushing with rose towards the aperture, and having deep rose veining.

The ventral sepal is smaller than the dorsal but similar in shape and colouring.

The staminode is roundish, white with green markings, and has a wide and deep lower incisure which forms two prominent, lateral, down-pointing lobes.

Flowers in summer.
Warm conditions.

P. wilhelminiae L. O. Williams 1942 (O.D.)

P. praestans subsp. *wilhelminiae* (Williams) M. W. Wood (O.R.)

Subgenus *Anotopedilum*. Section III *Coryopedilum*
New Guinea: West Irian, Balim River.

Found growing on sunny, grassy slopes at an elevation of 1700 metres (5500 feet).

Leaves are erect, 6 to 13 cm (2½ to 5 in) long and 1 to 2 cm (½ to ¾ in) wide. Oblong linear, obtuse, leathery and erect, with basal margins ciliate.

The flower scape is 10 to 30 cm (4 to 12 in) tall, erect, hirsute, and bears one or two flowers which are up to 10 cm (4 in) in height.

The dorsal sepal is yellowish-white veined with purple, ovate, keeled, and tapering to an acute apex. It is about 5 cm (2 in) long and 2 cm (¾ in) wide.

Petals are deep purple, narrow, lanceolate, and ciliate basally. They are 7 cm (3 in) long and 0.7 cm (⅜ in) wide, bearing warts at their tips.

The lip is pale yellow veined with purple and 3 to 4 cm ($1\frac{1}{4}$ to $1\frac{1}{2}$ in) long.

The ventral sepal is smaller than the dorsal and has two longitudinal dorsal keels.

The staminode is vertically ridged from base to apex, has two small calluses above the centre, and is pubescent on its lateral margins.

Warm conditions.

NOTE: The type specimen of *P. wilhelminiae* was recently examined at Harvard by James Asher Jr. and found to be totally different to *P. praestans*.

P. wolterianum (Krzl.) Stein 1895

Subgenus *Otopedilum*. Section XIII *Spathopetalum*
Coastal islands of south-west Cambodia, and Elephant Mountains, Cambodia.

Leaves are 9 to 15 cm ($3\frac{1}{2}$ to 6 in) long and 2 to 3 cm ($\frac{3}{4}$ to $1\frac{1}{4}$ in) wide. They are darkish green, tessellated with darker green. Distinctly keeled, and streaked with purple on basal undersides.

The flower scape is up to 50 cm (20 in) tall, brown, hirsute, and bearing a single flower.

The dorsal sepal is strongly recurved basally, with an acute and distinctly hooded apex. Apple green in colour, veined with darker green. The margins are slightly paler and there is some purple staining basally.

Petals are spatulate and droop to 45 degrees, with tips sometimes slightly up-turned. Green basally, with a mid-line of brownish-purple fading to pink apically. The basal parts of the upper margins are undulate, with brownish spots.

The lip is long, narrow, and pointed basally, with a distinct cleft in the rim. Greenish-cream basally, shading to brown towards the aperture, which has a narrow green margin. The in-folded side-lobes almost meet, and are greenish-yellow with minute reddish dots. The interior is pink, densely spotted with darker pink.

The ventral sepal is sharply keeled, long, narrow, and pale green.

The staminode is horizontally oval with a shallow lower incisure having outwardly directed lateral lobes.

Flowers in winter.

Intermediate conditions.

P. zieckianum Schoser 1967

Subgenus *Otopedilum*. Section *Mastersianum* Fowl.
Western New Guinea: Ararak Mountains.

Now lost to cultivation, this

species' distribution was reportedly limited to an area of only about half a hectare (one acre). It was in an area of very high humidity and rainfall at an elevation of 1200 metres (about 4000 feet).

The leaves are dark green, tessellated, have a conspicuous median line, and are 17 to 22 cm (7 to 9 in) long and 3 to 4 cm (1 to 1½ in) wide.

The flower scape is 25 to 28 cm (10 to 11 in) tall, brownish basally, merging upwards to purple, then green, and finally yellowish-green at the ovary. It is densely clothed with thick purple down, and bears a single flower up to 5 cm (2 in) wide.

The dorsal sepal is short and broad, 2.5 cm (1 in) wide, yellowish-green with a broad and distinct lighter coloured margin.

Petals are narrow basally but immediately become broadly spatulate. They are slightly cupped and ciliate on both margins. The upper halves are light green basally, shading to dark purplish-red at the tips, and the lower halves are brownish-yellow basally changing to purplish-red at the tips. The upper halves are spotted with dark brownish-black from their bases to almost mid-length.

The lip is greenish-purple and bears fine purple hairs. The rim of the aperture bears larger and more prominent hairs.

The ventral sepal is much smaller than the dorsal, is brownish-yellow in colour, and finely ciliate.

The staminode is whitish-yellow and bears a central, rounded, upper incisure.

Flowers in summer.

Warm conditions.

NEW SPECIES

*'P. dayanum-*like' (shortly to be described as *P. ceramensis*)
Subgenus *Otopedilum*. Section *Blepharopetalum*.

Sold by *Simanis Orchids*, Indonesia, this newly discovered species has not yet been formally described but has been included here as a point of interest.

Leaves are about 16 cm (6¼ in) long and 4 cm (1½ in) wide, notched at the tip, and have a prominent 'keel'. They are very light green with dark green tessellations on the upper surface, and the underside bears a slight reddish tinge basally, mainly on the mid-line.

The flower scape is about 30 cm (12 in) high, slender, single flowered, reddish-brown, and densely clothed with fine hairs.

The dorsal sepal is light green with very faint vertical striations of slightly darker green and vertically ovate with a sharply pointed apex, 2.5 cm (1 in) long and 1 cm (⅜ in) wide, the in-folded upper margins giving a hooded appearance. The front surface is glabrous and glossy, and the rear surface hirsute and dull.

The synsepalum is of the same shape and colour as the dorsal sepal, but slightly smaller.

The petals are horizontal and about 3.5 cm ($1\frac{1}{2}$ in) long; 6 mm ($\frac{1}{4}$ in) wide basally, widening to 1 cm ($\frac{3}{8}$ in) at three-quarter length, then tapering abruptly to a pointed apex. They are light green basally, changing to a bright rose-purple at about half length; both margins are pale green, and very sparsely clothed with fine hairs; sparse brownish spotting.

The lip is 2.5 cm (1 in) long, slender, swollen below mid-length to a maximum width of 1.2 cm ($\frac{1}{2}$ in);

light green basally, changing to a dark reddish-brown for most of its length, and bearing a light green margin around the aperture; the infolded side-lobes almost meet, and bear many small, glossy, reddish-brown warts.

The staminode is vertically ovate, with a shallow notch on the upper margin and a very deep central incisure on the lower margin framing a tiny, dark green uvula; light greenish-yellow with two dark green vertical lines.

The ovary is 3 cm ($1\frac{1}{4}$ in) long, slender, dark green, and hirsute.

The bract is about 1.5 cm ($\frac{5}{8}$ in) long, hirsute and light green with a reddish-brown apex.

Flowers in summer.

GLOSSARY

Acute Having an apex tapering to less than 90 degrees.

Apex The terminating point of a segment or leaf.

Apically Towards the apex.

Auricle A small lobe, usually ear-like.

Basally Towards the base.

Ciliate Fringed with hairs. Resembling eye-lashes.

Concave Hollowed out.

Convex Having a rounded surface.

Cordate Heart-shaped.

Dentate Toothed.

Epiphytic Growing on other plants but not as a parasite.

Glabrous Smooth, as opposed to hairy.

Hirsute Hairy, the hairs being long and distinct.

Linear Narrow, with parallel sides.

Lithophytic Growing on rocks.

Lobe A division of an organ.

Obtuse Blunt, having an angle of more than 90 degrees.

Pubescent Hairy, the hairs being soft and downy.

Re-curved Curved upwards or backwards.

Rhomboidal Quadrangular, with the lateral lobes obtuse.

Taxonomy Classification.

Terrestrial Growing in or on the ground.

Trilobate Three-lobed.

Tubercle Small, rounded swelling.

Undulate The margin bent into waves.

INDEX

Note: Where the taxonomy of species is contentious, taxa used by both the *Orchid Digest* and the *Orchid Review* are shown and designated by the abbreviations *O.D.* and *O.R.* respectively.